CASSELL'S **TECHNICAL** SERIES
CRAFT

Sheet Metal Drawing & Development

A. Yarwood

Cassell

London

Contents

CASSELL LTD

1 St Anne's Road, Eastbourne, East Sussex BN21 3UN

© A. Yarwood 1983

First published 1983

Printed and bound in Great Britain by Collins, Glasgow

British Library Cataloguing in Publication Data

Yarwood, Alfred
  Sheet metal drawing and development.
  1. Mechanical drawing
  I. Title
  604.2′4   T353

ISBN 0 304 30955 9

Preface

This book is based on the knowledge and experience resulting from the author's participation in education over many years. This includes the teaching of engineering drawing as the head of a technical department in a secondary modern school, as the head of a technical department in a grammar school and as the head of a technical drawing and technology department in a comprehensive school; as well as teaching/lecturing part-time in a technical college. The author is a Chief Examiner for Graphical Communication with a University school examinations department, a Chief Examiner for Technical Drawing with a C.S.E. examinations board, as well as a visiting moderator/examiner for Craftwork and Design at Ordinary and Advanced level with a large G.C.E. examinations board. He was a member of the working party responsible for producing the British Standards publication PD 308: *Engineering drawing practice for schools and colleges.*

The contents of this volume are designed to cover the requirements in drawing and development for the communication, pattern development and calculations studies envisaged by the City and Guilds syllabus 216 (Sheet Metal and Thin Plate Craft Studies) and, in part, 217 (Structural and Thick Plate Craft Studies).

The ability to be able to read and understand drawings is clearly a great asset which all craft students in any branch of engineering should endeavour to acquire. The book therefore not only sets out to cover the drawing and development sections of the City and Guilds syllabuses 216 and 217, but also aims at providing a course in drawing and development which will train the student to read and clearly understand the drawings which he will inevitably be using during his working life. With this aim in mind, a large number of drawings have been included throughout the book. These have been carefully selected to include examples taken from all parts of syllabuses 216 and 217. A large number of exercises for the student to work are also included. These are closely related to the pages of instructional material to help students to understand the principles of drawing and development involved.

Drawing and development are concerned mainly with line illustrations and a graphical understanding of the meaning of drawings is clearly desirable. Because of this the explanatory text in the form of words has been kept to the bare minimum consistent with a clear understanding of what is meant. Illustrations rather than words is a major theme of the book.

March 1983   A. Yarwood

Acknowledgements

The author wishes to record here his grateful appreciation to Mr A.E. Thomas, the Head of the Department of Automobile and Craft Engineering Department at the Luton College of Higher Education, for allowing photographs included in this book to be taken in the sheet metal department of the college. Also he would like to thank the City and Guilds of London Institute for allowing permission to reproduce questions taken from recent examination papers set on the subject of sheet metalwork.

1 Introduction

Lines used in drawings

The following types of lines are used in drawings throughout this book.

Thick lines

Thick lines show the outlines of views drawn in projection; the outlines of developments and patterns. Thick lines should be between twice and three times as thick as thin lines.

Thin lines

Thin lines are used to draw projection lines, dimension lines, centre lines and hidden detail lines. Thin lines should be about a half or a third as thick as thick lines.

Centre lines

Centre lines are thin broken lines consisting of alternate long and short dashes with spaces between them. The abbreviation Ḷ is occasionally placed on centre lines.

Hidden detail lines

Hidden detail lines are broken lines consisting of equal length short dashes, each about 3 mm long, with 3 mm long spaces between. Hidden detail lines are thin lines.

Section plane lines

Section plane lines are centre lines with their ends thickened.

Construction lines

These are thin fine lines which can be easily erased from a drawing.

Dimensions used in drawings

An example of methods of dimensioning is shown. The following abbreviations connected with dimensions are always placed *before* the figures of the dimension.

R — Radius
Ø — Diameter
□ — Square

Thick line

Thin line

Centre line

Hidden detail line

Section plane line

Construction line

Lines used in drawings

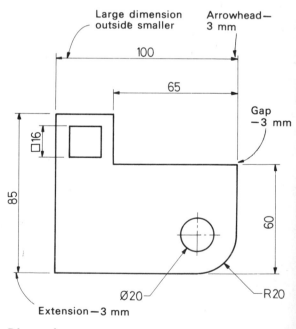

Dimensions

Dimension lines and projection lines for dimensions are thin lines. Arrow heads should touch projected lines and be about 3 mm long.

Geometrical terms

Square

Rectangle

Parallelogram

Diagonals of
square

Diagonals of rectangle

Diagonals of parallelogram

All sides
equal

Equilateral triangle

Two sides
equal

Isosceles triangle

All sides
unequal

Scalene triangle

Right angled triangle

Circumference
of circle

Radius of circle

Diameter of circle

Arc of circle

Chord of circle

Semicircle

Quadrant of circle

Sector of circle

360° in a circle

180° in a semicircle

Circle circumscribing
a hexagon

Circle inscribed in
a hexagon

Lines

To bisect a line
1   Draw AB of any length, say 77 mm long.
2   Set compass to about $\frac{2}{3}$ AB.
3   With the compass centred at A, draw two arcs C and D.
4   With the compass centred at B, draw two arcs E and F intersecting arcs C and D at G and H.
5   Join GH with a straight line.
6   J is the centre of AB. AB is said to be *bisected* at J.

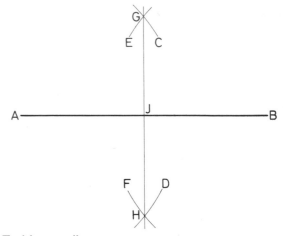

To bisect a line

To divide a line into equal parts
Line AB is to be divided into seven equal parts.

1   Draw AB of any length, say 95 mm long.
2   Draw AC at any angle to AB — about 30° is a good angle for this purpose.
3   Set compass to about $\frac{1}{7}$ of AB.
4   With the compass mark off seven equal spaces along AC.
5   Join B7.
6   Draw lines from points 1 to 6 along AC parallel to B7 using a ruler and set square (as shown).
7   AB is now divided into seven equal parts.

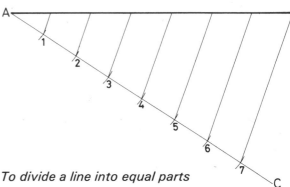

To divide a line into equal parts

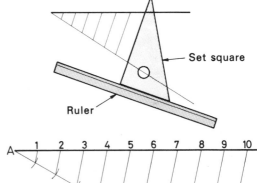

To divide a line into twelve equal parts
In constructing developments for sheet metalwork it is necessary to know how to divide a line into twelve equal parts. The procedure is the same as for dividing a line into any number of equal parts.

1   Draw AB 127 mm long.
2   Draw AC at an angle to AB.
3   Set a compass to about $\frac{1}{12}$ of AB.
4   With the compass mark off twelve equal spaces along AC.
5   Join the twelfth point D on AC to B.
6   Draw lines from the other eleven points on AC parallel to BD.
7   AB is now divided into twelve equal parts.

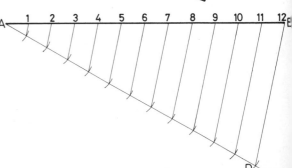

To divide a line into twelve equal parts

Angles

To construct an angle with a protractor
An angle, ABC, of 143° is to be constructed.

1 Draw line AB.
2 Place a protractor with its base line lying exactly on AB and with its base line centre positioned at B.
3 At 143° on the protractor make a mark with a pencil.
4 Draw line BC from B to the pencil mark.
5 Angle ABC is 143°.

Note: An angle less than 90° (a right angle) is said to be an *acute* angle.

An angle greater than 90°, but less than 180°, is said to be an *obtuse* angle.

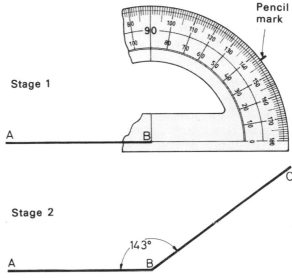

Stage 1

Stage 2

To construct an angle with a protractor

To bisect any angle
The following applies to both the examples shown in drawings 1 and 2. Drawing 1 shows the bisection of an acute angle. Drawing 2 shows the bisection of an obtuse angle.

1 With the aid of a protractor construct an acute angle of 56° and an obtuse angle of 126°.
2 Set a compass to about 25 mm.
3 With the compass centred at E draw an arc to cross DE at G and cross EF at H.
4 Reset the compass if thought necessary.
5 With the compass centred at G draw arc J.
6 Without altering the compass, and centred at H, draw arc K to intersect arc J.
7 Draw a line through the intersection of the arcs and produce to L.
8 EL bisects angle DEF in both cases. Angle DEL = Angle LEF.

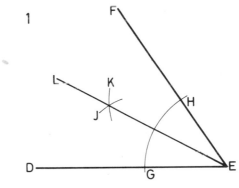

To bisect an acute angle

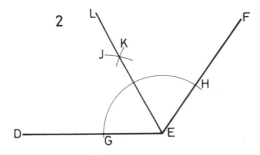

To bisect an obtuse angle

To construct an angle of 60°

1 Draw line AB — say 60 mm long.
2 Set a compass to about 30 mm.
3 With the compass centred at B draw an arc to cut AB at D.
4 Without altering the compass and centred at D, draw arc E across the arc from B.
5 Join BE and produce to C.
6 Angle ABC is 60°.

Note: An angle of 60° can also be drawn with the aid of a 30°, 60° set square.

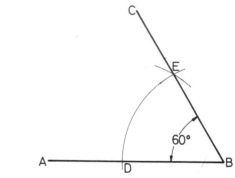

To construct an angle of 60°

To construct an angle of 30°

1 Construct an angle of 60° — angle FGH.
2 Bisect angle FGH to give angle FGL.
3 Angle FGL is 30°

Note: An angle of 30° can also be drawn with the aid of a 30°, 60° set square.

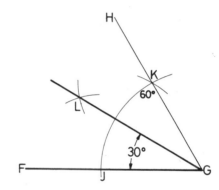

To construct an angle of 30°

To construct an angle of 90°

1 Draw MN — say 75 mm long.
2 Set a compass to about 30 mm.
3 With the compass centred at N draw an arc to cross MN at O.
4 Without altering the compass, draw arc P with the compass centred at O, and arc Q with the compass centred at P.
5 The compass can now be reset if thought necessary.
6 With the compass centred first at P and then at Q draw two arcs to intersect at R.
7 Join NR and produce.
8 Angle MNR is 90°.

Note

1 Look at this construction carefully. It will be seen that it really consists of the addition of 60° and 30° angles.
2 An angle of 45° can be constructed by bisecting an angle of 90°.
3 Angles of 90° can also be drawn with the aid of a set square, or in a workshop, with the aid of a try square.

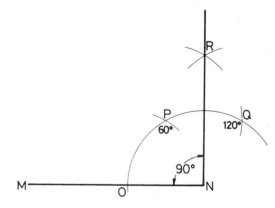

To construct an angle of 90°

Regular polygons

A polygon is a figure with a number of straight sides. If all its sides and all its angles are equal to each other, a polygon is said to be *regular*. A regular *hexagon* has six equal sides and each of its six angles is 120°. A regular *octagon* has eight equal sides and each of its angles is 135°.

To divide a circle into six equal parts
1   Draw a circle of, say, radius 40 mm. Its centre is O.
2   Without altering the compass, and starting at any point on the circumference of the circle, step off arcs around the circle.
3   If this is carried out carefully, it will be found that the sixth arc crosses the circle at the point where the compass was first centred.
4   Try this with circles of various radii. It will be found that the radius can *always* be stepped off exactly six times around its circle.

   Note: From this construction, it can be seen that the angle AOB must be 60°. This is because the circle contains 360° and AOB is $\frac{1}{6}$ of the circle.

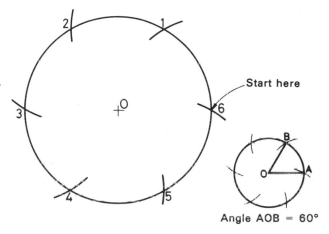

To divide a circle into six equal parts

To draw a regular hexagon of a given side length
1   Take the side length as 30 mm. Draw a circle of radius 30 mm.
2   Draw a horizontal line across the circle through its centre O.
3   Without altering the compass, mark off arcs B and F (centred at A) and C and E (centred at D).
4   Join AB, BC, CD, DE, EF and FA to complete the regular hexagon.

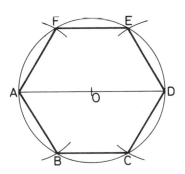

To draw a regular hexagon of a given side length

To draw a regular octagon of given side length

1 Take the side length as 25 mm. Draw AB 25 mm long.
2 With the aid of a 45° set square draw angles of 135° to AB at A and at B.
3 Set a compass to 25 mm and mark off arcs from A and from B to give H and C.
4 At C and at H draw verticals with the set square.
5 Mark off D and G with the compass from C and H.
6 Continue in this manner to complete the regular octagon.

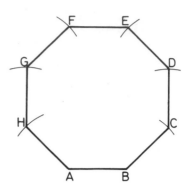

To draw a regular octagon of a given side length

Note: The smaller drawing shows how a regular octagon can be drawn within a given square.

1 Draw the diagonals of the square.
2 Draw arcs of radius AO, BO, CO and DO to give the side lengths of the regular octagon.
3 Complete the octagon.

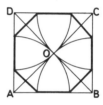

To draw an octagon in a square

Circles

To divide a circle into twelve equal parts

1 Draw a circle of, say, 70 mm diameter (set compass to 35 mm).
2 Draw horizontal and vertical lines through O, the centre of the circle.
3 Do not alter the setting of the compass.
4 With the compass centred at the ends of each of the lines drawn across the circle draw arcs across its circumference. From 1 draw arcs 3 and 11; from 4 draw arcs 2 and 6; from 7 draw arcs 5 and 9; from 10 draw arcs 8 and 12.
5 The circle is now divided into twelve equal parts.

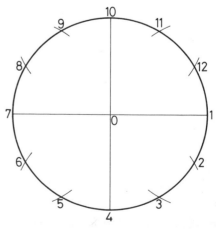

To divide a circle into twelve equal parts

To divide a circle into twelve equal parts — another method

1 Draw a circle of, say, 60 mm diameter (radius 30 mm).
2 Draw horizontal and vertical lines through its centre O.
3 With the aid of a 30°, 60° set square draw lines at 30° and 60° through O across the circumference of the circle.
4 The circle is now divided into twelve equal parts.

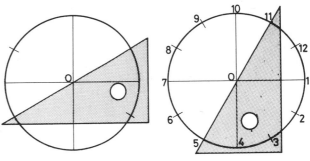

To divide a circle into twelve equal parts: another method

Straight line tangent to a circle

If a straight line touches a circle it is said to be *tangential* to the circle. The line AB is a *tangent* to the circle of centre O.

The tangent AB touches the circle at T. T is the *point of tangency* of the line to the circle. If a line is drawn from T to the circle centre O, then the angle ATO is 90° — a right angle.

Thus to find a point of tangency a right angle must be drawn to the tangential line to pass through the circle centre.

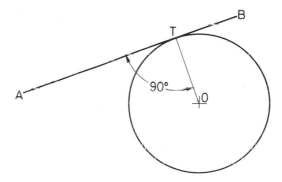

Straight line tangent to a circle

Triangles

When developing patterns for sheet metal articles it is necessary to know how to draw triangles accurately. In the chapter on Development by Triangulation (pages 126 to 146) it will be seen that many development patterns rely completely on an ability to construct accurate triangles. The most common triangle used in development by triangulation is the *scalene* triangle. A *scalene triangle* is one in which all three sides are *unequal* in length and all three angles are of *unequal* size.

To construct a scalene triangle

Let the triangle be ABC, in which AB = 75 mm; AC = 115 mm; BC = 105 mm.

1 Draw AB 75 mm long.
2 Set a compass to AC (115 mm).
3 With the compass centred at A draw an arc.
4 Set the compass to BC (105 mm).
5 With the compass centred at B draw an arc to cross that from A. The intersection of the two arcs gives C.
6 Join AC and BC to complete the triangle.

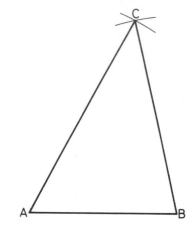

To construct a scalene triangle

To construct an isosceles triangle

An *isosceles* triangle is one in which two sides are of equal length and two angles are of equal size.

Let the triangle be DEF in which DE = 70 mm; DF = EF = 110 mm.

1 Draw DE 70 mm long.
2 Set a compass to DF (110 mm).
3 With the compass centred first at D, then at E, draw arcs intersecting at F.
4 Join DF and EF to complete the triangle.

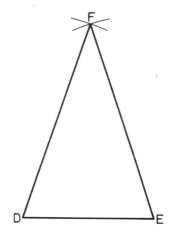

To construct an isosceles triangle

To construct a right angled triangle

A right angled triangle is one in which one of the angles is 90°.

Let the triangle be GHJ in which GH = 115 mm; HJ = 70 mm; angle GHJ = 90°.

1 Draw GH 115 mm long.
2 Draw a right angle at H — by construction or with a set square.
3 Set a compass to 70 mm and from H mark off J.
4 Join HJ to complete the triangle.

Equilateral triangle

The fourth type of triangle is the *equilateral*. In an equilateral triangle all sides are of equal length and each angle is 60°.

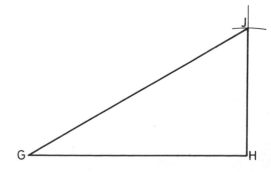

To construct a right angled triangle

2 First and Third Angle orthographic projections

The most common method of showing the precise shapes of articles made by engineering firms is by means of working drawings drawn in orthographic projection. In sheet metalworking the majority of working drawings are made in what is known as *First Angle* projection. First Angle projection has been adopted for all drawings in this book.

Another method of projection — *Third Angle* projection — is shown in drawings on pages 16 and 17. The two methods of First and Third Angles are similar except that the positions of end views and plans in relation to front views are different.

For the purpose of describing First Angle projection a twisted rectangular duct transformer has been taken as an example. A pictorial drawing of the duct is shown on this page. Six drawings numbered 1 to 6 on this page and on pages 14 and 15 describe the method of obtaining two-view and three-view drawings of the twisted rectangular duct transformer.

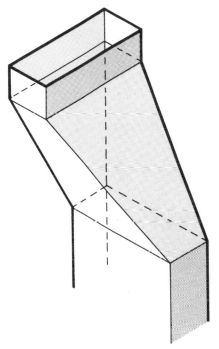

A twisted rectangular duct transformer

First angle projection

Drawing 1

Two planes — a *Vertical Plane* and a *Horizontal Plane* — are set at right angles to each other. Planes at right angles to each other are said to be *orthogonal*.

1

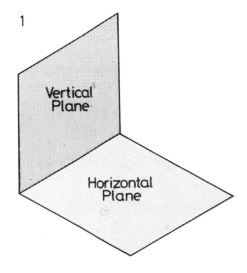

Vertical Plane

Horizontal Plane

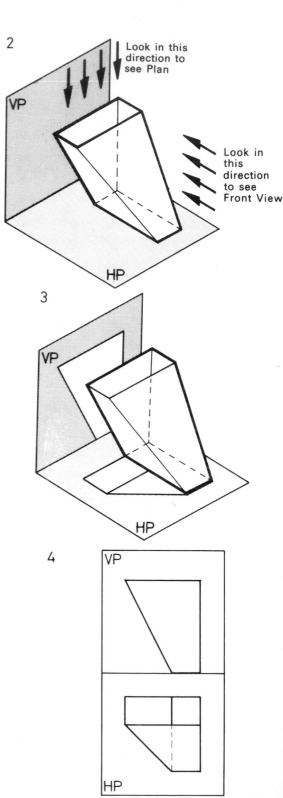

Drawing 2

The transformer is imagined as being placed on the Horizontal Plane. It is then viewed from the front and from above.

Drawing 3

What is seen when viewed in the direction to see the transformer's Front View is drawn on to the Vertical Plane. What is seen when viewed in the direction to see its Plan is drawn on the Horizontal Plane.

Drawing 4

The transformer is taken away from its position on the Horizontal Plane and one of the two planes is swung through 90° so as to lie in the same plane as the other. This produces a two-view drawing of the transformer showing a Front View and a Plan, the Plan lying *below* the Front View.

Drawing 5

To obtain a third view, the two planes are replaced into their orthogonal position (at right angles to each other) and a second Vertical Plane placed so as to be at right angles to both the first Vertical Plane and the Horizontal Plane. The transformer is then viewed in the direction shown and what is seen projected on to the second Vertical Plane.

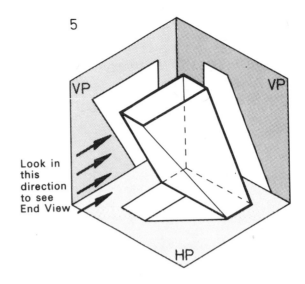

Drawing 6

All three planes are now swung so as to lie in the same flat plane to each other. The result is a three-view drawing showing a Front View, an End View and a Plan.

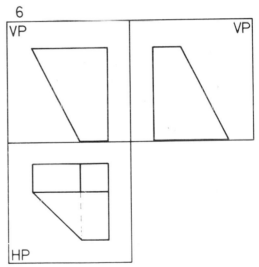

Note

1   The term 'elevation' is frequently used in place of the term 'view'. *Front elevation* means the same as front view and *end elevation* means the same as end view.
2   In First Angle projection the plan as seen from above lies *below* the front view.
3   In First Angle projection the end view should be drawn on the opposite side from the direction of viewing.

Third Angle Projection

Another form of projection, based on the same general principles as is First Angle projection but with the object being drawn placed in a different position relative to the Horizontal Plane and Vertical Planes, is Third Angle projection.

Third Angle projection is sometimes called 'American projection' because engineering drawings made in the USA are commonly drawn in Third Angle. Students will find they may have to use Third Angle drawings particularly when engaged on work originating in the USA. Many firms in Europe are also now using Third Angle drawings.

Six drawings numbered 1 to 6 on pages 16 and 17 describe the method of obtaining two-view and three-view Third Angle projections of the twisted rectangular duct already shown on page 14.

Drawing 1

Two planes — a *Vertical Plane* (VP) and a
Horizontal Plane (HP) — are set at right angles
to each other.

Drawing 2

The transformer is imagined as being placed in
the space formed by the two planes. Note that
in the case of Third Angle projection the object
does *not* rest on the HP. The transformer is
viewed from the front and from above *through
the planes.*

Drawing 3

What is seen through the VP when viewed in
the direction to see the Front View is drawn on
the VP. What is seen when viewed in the
direction to see its plan, through the HP, is
drawn on the HP.

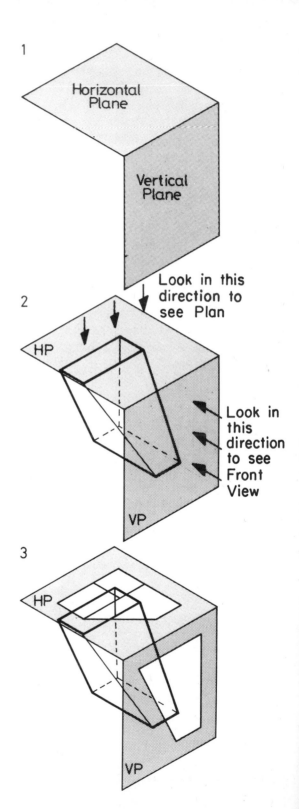

Drawing 4

The transformer is taken away from its position between the HP and VP and one of the two planes is swung through 90° so as to lie in the same plane as the other. This produces a two-view drawing of the transformer showing a Front View and a Plan, the Plan lying *above* the Front View.

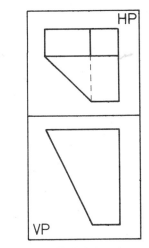

Front view and plan in Third Angle projection

Drawing 5

To obtain a third view, the two planes are replaced in their original positions (at right angles to each other) and a second Vertical Plane placed so as to be at right angles to both the first Vertical Plane and to the Horizontal Plane. The transformer is then viewed in a direction so as to see an End View through the second Vertical Plane. This End View is then drawn on the second Vertical Plane.

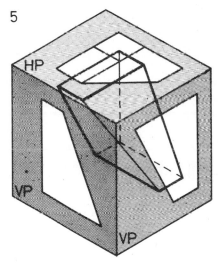

Drawing 6

All three planes are now swung so as to lie in the same flat plane to each other. The result is a three-view drawing showing a Front View, an End View and a Plan.

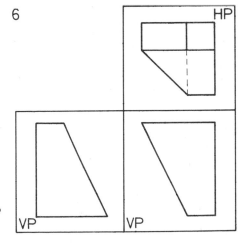

Front view, end view and plan in Third Angle projection

Note

1   In Third Angle projection the plan as seen from above lies *above* the Front View.
2   In Third Angle projection the End View should be drawn on the *same* side of the Front View as the direction of viewing.

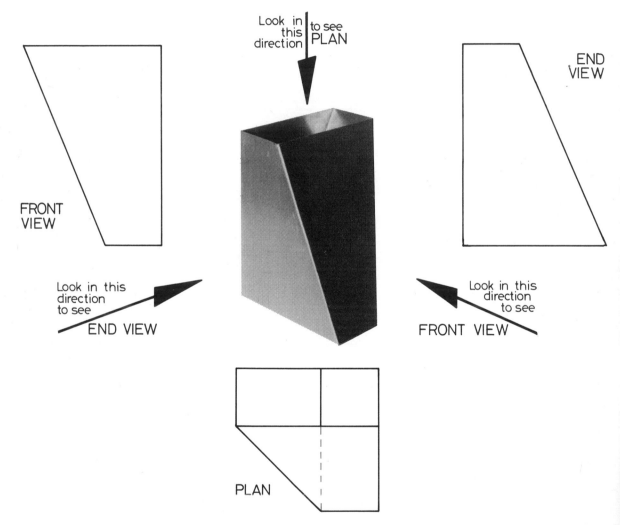

This drawing shows, in a different manner to that described on pages 13 to 15, the methods of obtaining a First Angle orthographic projection.

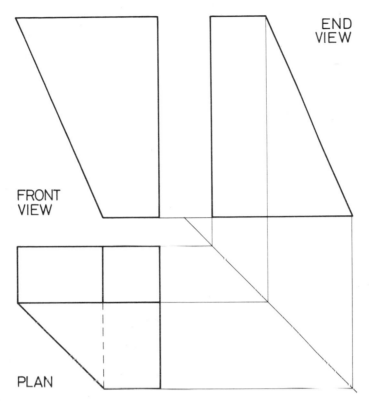

FRONT VIEW

END VIEW

PLAN

First Angle projection of the twisted rectangular duct. Note that in a working drawing it is not usual practice to label the views.

Setting Out a Three-View Drawing

The drawings 1 to 4 show the stages of setting out a three-view First Angle projection of the twisted rectangular duct transformer.

Drawing 1

1 Draw a base line AB. At C draw CD at 45° to AB.
2 On AB draw a rectangle of overall front view height by overall front view width.
3 From the front view project vertically downwards to obtain the overall rectangle for the plan. In this example the plan rectangle is a square.
4 Project horizontally from the plan on to line CD and then vertically up to obtain overall width of the end view.

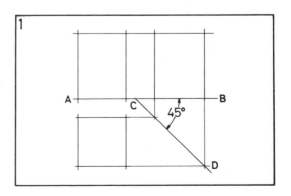

5 Project horizontally from the upper edge of the front view rectangle to obtain the height of the end view.

Drawing 2

1 Fill in details of the plan.
2 The outline of the plan can be 'lined-in' with thick outline lines.

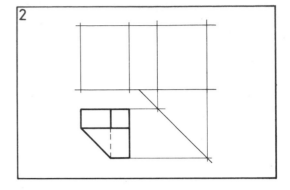

Drawing 3

1 Project details from the plan upwards into the front view.
2 The outline of the front view can be 'lined-in'.
3 Project details from the plan on the line CD and then upwards into the end view.

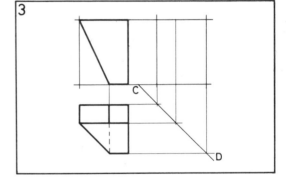

Drawing 4

1 The end view can now be 'lined-in'.
2 All construction lines can now be erased.

Note: If this drawing was intended as a working drawing details of dimensions would now be added.

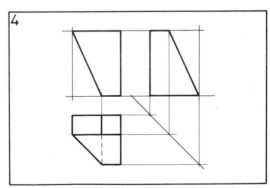

3 Prisms, cylinders, pyramids and cones

All the given examples of prisms, cylinders, pyramids and cones are taken from shells, as if made from sheet materials.

Right prisms

If a cross-sectional cut is taken at any point across any *right prism* at right angles to its central axis the outline of the section is always of the same shape for that particular prism. Thus there are such forms of right prisms as square prisms and so on, whose cross-sectional outline is defined by their names.

If a right prism is cut at an angle other than a right angle to its central axis, what remains is known as a *truncated* prism. If the cut is made parallel to the base, what remains is known as the *frustum* of the prism.

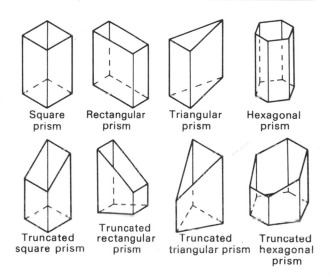

Square prism   Rectangular prism   Triangular prism   Hexagonal prism

Truncated square prism   Truncated rectangular prism   Truncated triangular prism   Truncated hexagonal prism

Orthographic projections of right prisms
Four examples of three-view orthographic projections of truncated prisms are given. Small pictorial drawings showing the prisms placed in the viewing position between a horizontal plane and two vertical planes are also shown.

Front view, end view and plan of truncated rectangular prism
The prism is of rectangular section 50 mm by 20 mm. Its height is 60 mm and the truncation is at 30° to the horizontal.

1 Draw a base line and a 45° projection line.
2 Draw the plan — a rectangle 50 mm by 20 mm.
3 Project a front view from the plan.
4 Project an end view from the front view and from the plan using the 45° projection line.

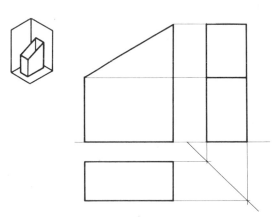

Front view, end view and plan of truncated rectangular prism

Front view, end view and plan of truncated square prism

The prism is of square section of 50 mm sides. Its height is 60 mm. The upper truncation is at 30° to the horizontal, the lower truncation is at 15° to the horizontal.

1   Draw a base line and a 45° projection line.
2   Draw the plan — a square of 50 mm sides.
3   Project a front view from the plan.
4   Project an end view from the front view and plan with the aid of the 45° projection line.

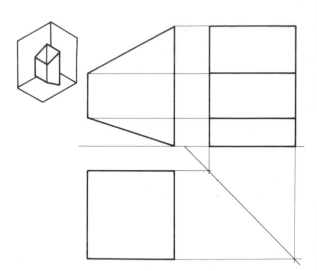

Front view, end view and plan of truncated square prism

Front view, end view and plan of truncated triangular prism

The prism is of equilateral triangular section of sides 35 mm long. Its height is 70 mm. The truncation is at 45°.

1   Draw a base line and a 45° projection line.
2   Draw the plan — an equilateral triangle of 35 mm sides.
3   Project a front view from the plan.
4   Project the end view from the plan and front view.

Note: The truncated face in the end view becomes an equilateral triangle of the same size as the plan. This is because the truncation is at 45°.

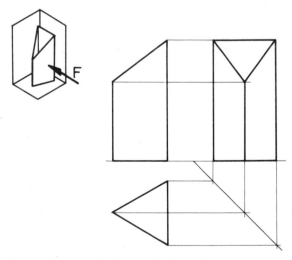

Front view, end view and plan of truncated triangular prism

Front view, end view and plan of truncated hexagonal prism

The prism is of right hexagonal section with sides 25 mm long. Its height is 70 mm. The truncation is at 30° to the horizontal.

Note: In order to see the truncated face in the end view, the end view itself is placed on the *left* of the front view. In the small drawing of the prism between planes, F indicates the direction of viewing to obtain a front view.

1 Draw a base line and a 45° projection line.
2 Draw the plan — a regular hexagon of 25 mm sides.
3 Project a front view from the plan.
4 Project an end view from the plan and front view.

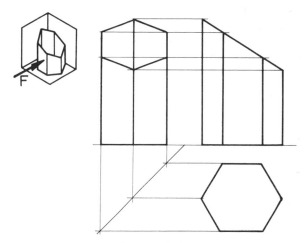

Front view, end view and plan of truncated hexagonal prism

Right cylinders

A right cylinder is a form of prism in which the cross-sectional outline taken at right angles to a central axis is circular in outline. Cylinders are important in sheet metalworking because of their common use in pipework of all kinds.

Front view, end view and plan of a cylinder

The cylinder is of diameter 40 mm and height 30 mm.

1 Draw a base line and a 45° projection line.
2 Draw a plan — a circle of 40 mm diameter.
3 Project front views and end views — both rectangles of side lengths 40 mm by 30 mm.

Note: Centre lines should be drawn at right angles through the centres of circles of circular parts. The central axis of circular parts should also carry a centre line in front and end views.

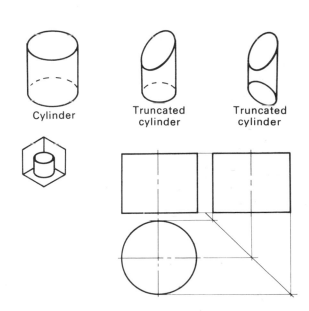

Front view, end view and plan of a cylinder

Front view, end view and plan of a truncated cylinder

The arrows marked F indicate the direction of viewing to see front views.

The cylinder is of diameter 46 mm and height 65 mm, truncated at 30° to the horizontal.

1 Draw a plan — a circle of diameter 46 mm.
2 Project a front view from the plan.
3 Divide circle of plan into twelve equal parts.
4 Taking each of the twelve divisions in turn project into the end view from the plan and front view as shown in the sequence numbered 1, 2, 3 and 4. Where the projection line from point 2 on the front view meets the projection line 3 from the 45° line, a point — 4 — is found on the end view.
5 When the twelve points from the plan and front view have been projected into the end view following the sequence 1, 2, 3 and 4, the twelve points in the end view are joined in a smooth curve. In this example the curve is an *ellipse*.

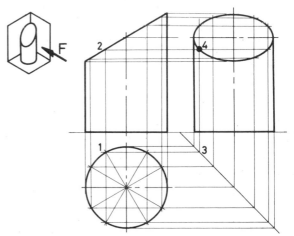

Front view, end view and plan of a truncated cylinder

Front view, end view and plan of a truncated cylinder

The cylinder is of diameter 36 mm and height 80 mm, truncated at 45° one end and at 30° to the horizontal at its other end.

Note: The end view is drawn on the left of the front view to enable the end view to show the truncated faces.

The method of drawing the three views is the same as for the example above, following the sequence of projection given by 1, 2, 3, 4 and 5.

Note: In the end view the upper truncated face shows as a *circle* of 36 mm diameter. This is because the truncation is at 45°. The lower truncated face shows as an *ellipse* in the end view.

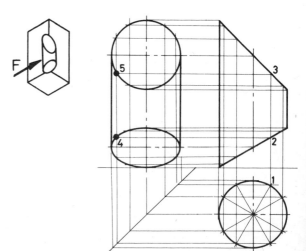

Front view, end view and plan of a truncated cylinder

Right pyramids

The pyramid is another form found in articles made from sheet metal. Many hoppers are pyramids in form and some connectors and transformers are also based on pyramids.

If sections are taken at right angles to the axis of a pyramid, each section is of *similar* outline but of differing edge lengths, becoming smaller as the sectional cuts are made nearer to the *apex* of the pyramid.

Orthographic projection of right pyramids
Note: The arrows marked F indicate the direction of viewing to obtain a front view.

Front view, end view and plan of a square pyramid
The pyramid is of a square base of 40 mm sides and of height 60 mm.

1 Draw base line and 45° projection line.
2 Draw the plan — a square of sides 40 mm with both diagonals included.
3 Project a front view from the plan.
4 Project an end view from the front view and plan.

> *Note*: Each of the two views — front and end — is an isosceles triangle.

Front view, end view and plan of a truncated square pyramid
The pyramid is of a square base of 40 mm sides and of height 60 mm, truncated at 45° at 36 mm at the highest point.

1 Draw a base line and a 45° projection line.
2 Draw the outline of the plan with its diagonals in construction lines.
3 Project the front view from the plan. Draw the 45° truncation line on the front view.
4 Project the plan of the truncated surface back into the plan.
5 Now project an end view from the front view and plan.

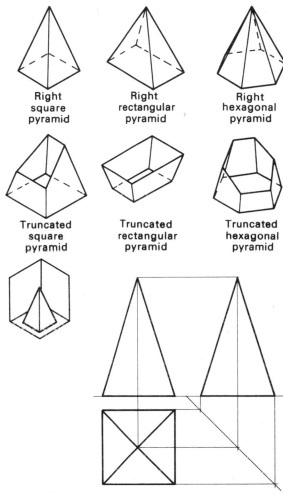

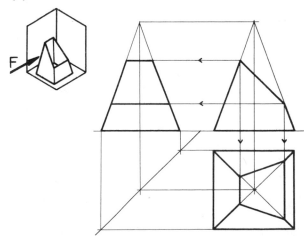

Front view, end view and plan of a square pyramid

Front view, end view and plan of a truncated square pyramid

Front view, end view and plan of a truncated hexagonal pyramid

The pyramid is of a regular hexagonal base of sides 20 mm long and the height is 60 mm. It is truncated at 30° to the horizontal, with the highest point of truncation 30 mm above the base.

1 Draw a base line and a 45° projection line.
2 Draw the outline of the plan — a hexagon of 20 mm sides. Draw the diagonals of this hexagon in construction lines.
3 Project a front view from the plan. Draw the truncation line of the front view.
4 Project the plan of the truncated surface from the front view back into the plan.
5 Project an end view from the front view and plan.

Note: Arrows on the projection lines of the two above examples show the direction in which the projections must take place.

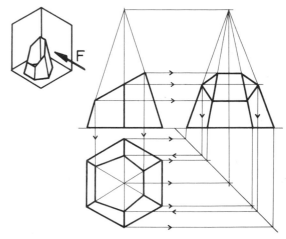

Front view, end view and plan of a truncated hexagonal pyramid

Right cones

Right cones are another example of three-dimensional geometrical forms of importance to sheet metalworkers. Many connectors and transformer pieces are of conical form as are many containers and some hoppers. A section taken at right angles to the axis of a right cone is circular in outline. The diameters of such cross-sectional outlines become smaller the nearer to the apex the section is taken.

Orthographic projections of right cones

Three examples of three-view First Angle projections of right cones are given. The third example is described in three stages on page 28.

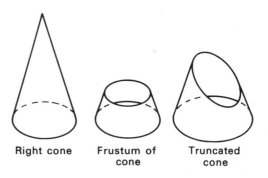

Right cone   Frustum of   Truncated
                     cone   cone

Front view, end view and plan of a right cone

The cone is of base diameter 44 mm and of height 60 mm.

1 Draw a base line and a 45° projection line.
2 Draw the plan — a circle of diameter 44 mm. Note the centre lines passing vertically and horizontally through the circle centre.
3 Project a front view from the plan.
4 Project an end view from the plan and front view.

Note: The front and end views are isosceles triangles.

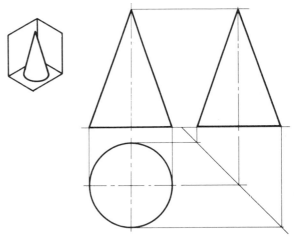

Front view, end view and plan of right cone

Front view, end view and plan of frustum of cone

The cone is of the same size as the previous example but cut at right angles to the axis, 20 mm above the base.

1 Draw a base line and a 45° projection line.
2 Draw the outline of the plan — a circle of 44 mm diameter.
3 Project a front view from the plan and draw the cutting plane line.
4 Project the ends of the cutting plane line back into the plan to determine the diameter of the upper surface of the frustum in the plan. Draw the circle of the surface.
5 Project the end view from the front view and plan.

Note: If a right cone is cut by a section plane parallel to the base, the cut surface is circular in outline. Use can be made of this fact in constructing plans of surfaces cut by planes of angles other than those parallel to the base.

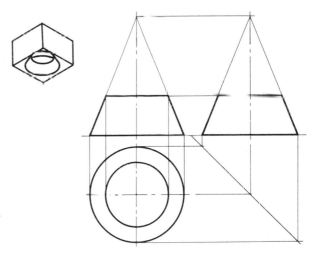

Front view, end view and plan of frustum of cone

Front view, end view and plan of truncated cone

The drawing shows a cone of base diameter 50 mm and height 60 mm cut by a truncating surface at 30° to the horizontal, with its highest point at 30 mm above the base.

Stage 1

1 Construct a front view, end view and plan of the whole cone before truncation.
2 Add the truncation line to the front view.
3 Draw three horizontal lines — numbered 1, 2 and 3 on the drawing — across both front and end views. These three lines represent sectional cuts taken parallel to the base.
4 Project the diameter of each of these horizontal sectional cuts into the plan and draw the three circles they represent.

Stage 2

5 At the points where the horizontal section plane lines 1, 2 and 3 are cut by the 30° truncation line project into the plan to the circles representing the horizontal plane lines.
6 Project these points from the plan and front view into the end view.

   Note: All the points so found are shown by tiny circles in the plan and end view.

Stage 3

Draw smooth curves through the points so obtained — that is through the points shown by the tiny circles.

Note: The curve outlines in the plan and end view of the truncated surface are both *ellipses*.

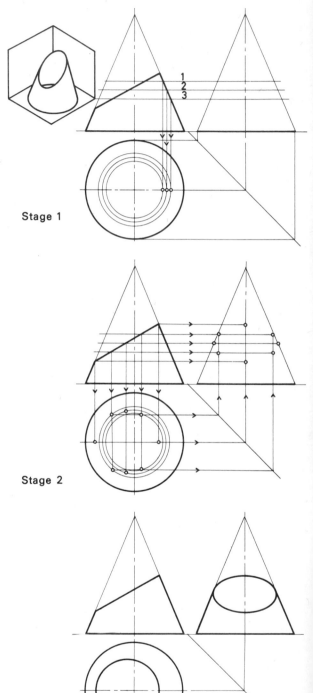

Stage 1

Stage 2

Stage 3

Front view, end view and plan of truncated cone

Front view, end view and plan of truncated cone: another method of construction

A different method of constructing the plans and end views of truncated cones is given in three stages.

Stage 1

1 Draw front view, end view and plan, before truncation, to the dimensions given.
2 Add the truncating line.
3 Divide the plan circle into twelve equal parts to give points 1 to 12.
4 Join points 1 to 12 to the apex A in the plan.
5 Project points 1 to 12 from the plan to the bottom lines of front and end views.
6 Join the points 1 to 12 in front and end views to the apex A.

Stage 2

At the points 1 to 7 where the sloping lines meet the truncating line in the front view, project into the plan and end view to give points A to M in both views.

Stage 3

Join points A to M in plan and end view by fair freehand curves to complete the required views.

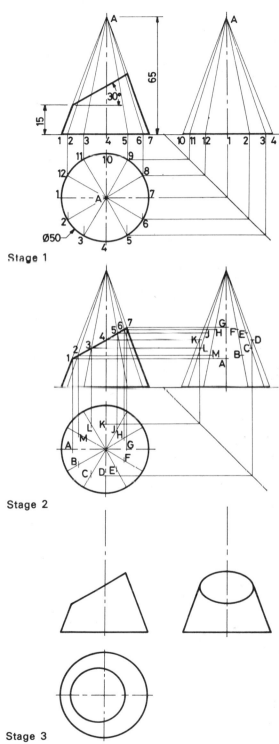

Stage 1

Stage 2

Stage 3

Front view, end view and plan of truncated cone: another method of construction

Front view, end view and plan of truncated cone: a worked example

The cone base has a diameter of 64 mm and a height of 90 mm, truncated at 45° as shown.

This example follows the construction described on page 29.

1 Draw front view, end view and plan of the full cone before truncation.
2 Add the truncating line.
3 Divide the plan circle into twelve equal parts to give points 1 to 12 in the plan.
4 Join points 1 to 12 to the apex A in the plan.
5 Project points 1 to 12 from the plan on to the base lines of the front and end views.
6 Join these points to the apex A in both views.
7 Where these sloping lines meet the truncating line of the front view, project on to the lines A1 to A12 in plan and end view.
8 Draw fair freehand curves through the intersections so obtained to complete the end view and plan.

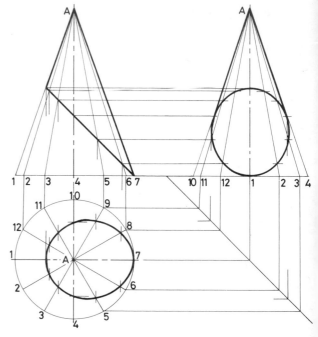

Front view, end view and plan of a truncated cone: a worked example

Front view, end view and plan of a right cone cut by a vertical plane: a worked example

The cone base diameter is 64 mm and its height is 120 mm. The vertical cutting plane is 10 mm from the axis of the cone.

This example also follows the construction described on page 29.

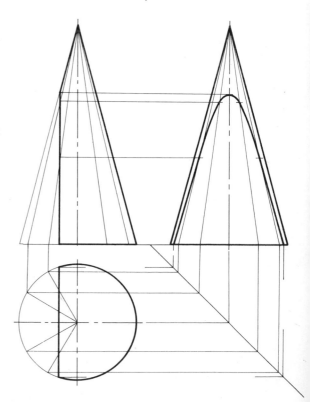

Front view, end view and plan of a right cone cut by a vertical plane: a worked example

Oblique forms

Orthographic projections of oblique forms
If the central axis of the three-dimensional form is at an angle to the base, sectional cuts made at an angle to the axis but parallel to the base will have outlines the same as, or similar to, the base.

Front view, end view and plan of an oblique hexagonal prism
The base is a regular hexagon of sides 15 mm, with an axis sloping at 60° and the vertical height is 40 mm.

1 Construct the base hexagon in plan.
2 Project the corners of the hexagon to the base line.
3 From these points on the base line construct the front view.
4 Project the top of the prism from the front view to the plan.
5 Complete the plan.
6 Project an end view from the front view and plan.

Front view, end view and plan of an oblique cylinder
The cylinder has a base diameter of 25 mm. The axis slopes at 45° and the vertical height is 40 mm.

The method of constructing the required three views follows a procedure similar to that given for the oblique hexagonal prism above, except that the plan consists of circles joined by tangential lines.

Front view, end view and plan of frustum of oblique cone
The cone is of a base diameter 30 mm and vertical height 40 mm with a central axis sloping at 60° to the base. Truncation is 25 mm parallel to the base.

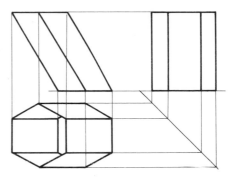

Front view, end view and plan of oblique hexagonal prism

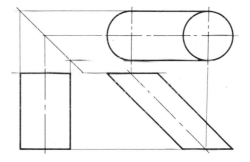

Front view, end view and plan of oblique cylinder

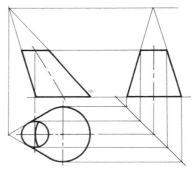

Front view, end view and plan of frustum of oblique cone

1 Draw the base circle in plan.
2 Project the diameter of the base on to the base line.
3 Draw the 60° central axis and mark off vertical height.
4 Draw slope sides of cone to apex.
5 Mark and draw horizontal truncation line.
6 Project diameter of truncated surface into plan.
7 Complete plan.
8 Project end view from front view and plan.

Exercises

1–10 The pictorial drawings 1 to 10 are of geometrical three-dimensional forms. They have been drawn on an isometric grid.

The isometric grid is made up of a series of triangles whose sides are *all* 10 mm long. The dimensions of each of the geometrical forms shown can be obtained by counting the number of triangle sides along the 30° lines of the grid and along the vertical lines of the grid. Thus, the rectangular prism numbered 1 has a width of four triangle sides = 4 × 10 mm = 40 mm; a depth of two triangle sides = 2 × 10 mm = 20 mm; a height of five triangle sides = 5 × 10 mm = 50 mm. The prism is therefore a right rectangular prism of sides 40 mm by 20 mm and 50 mm high.

Take each of the geometrical forms in turn and draw the front view, end view and plan of each of them.

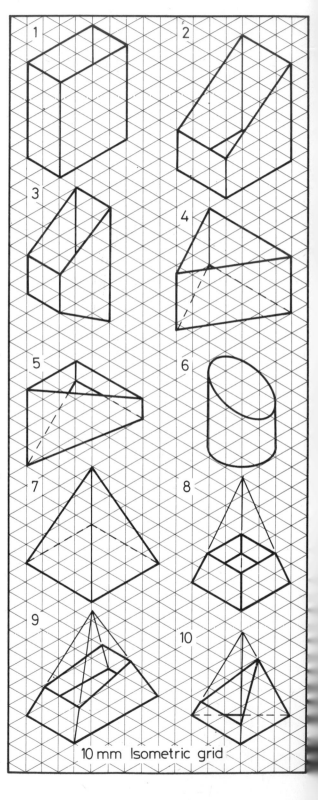

10 mm Isometric grid

11–20 Construct the front view, end view and plan of each of the geometrical forms shown.

Readers attempting Questions 21, 22, 23, 25 and 26 are advised to copy the given drawings to a scale of 1:1 (full size) before attempting the solutions.

21 Using the given centre line, construct a plan view of the sheet metal chute shown. (*City and Guilds*)

22 Complete the front elevation and end view of the right cone shown. (*City and Guilds*)

21

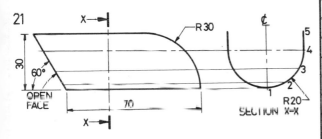

PLAN VIEW

22

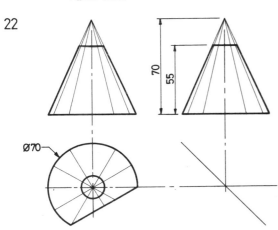

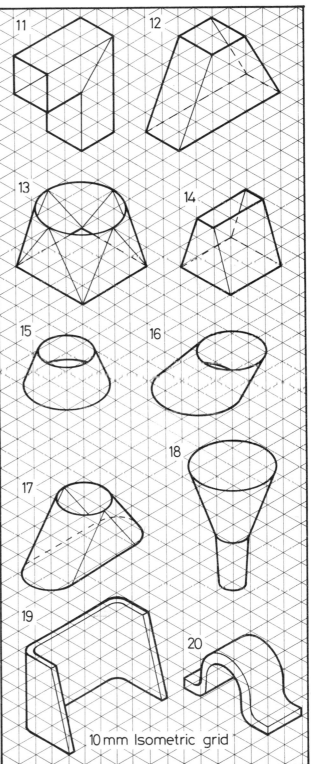

10 mm Isometric grid

23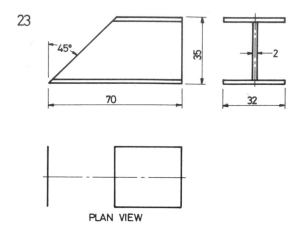

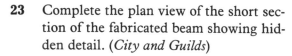

PLAN VIEW

24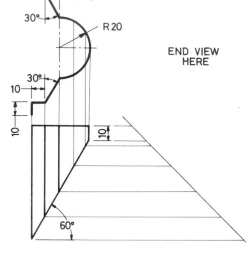

END VIEW
HERE

25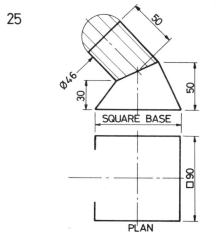

26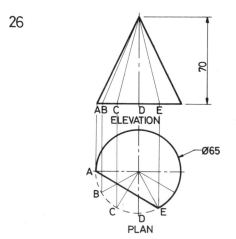

23 Complete the plan view of the short section of the fabricated beam showing hidden detail. (*City and Guilds*)

24 Copy the given drawing of a sheet metal moulded corner. Add an end view in the position indicated.

25 Complete the plan view of the symmetrical hood shown. (*City and Guilds*)

26 A right cone is cut by a plane A–E as shown in the given plan. Complete the elevation showing the projected shape of the conic section at the plane A–E. (*City and Guilds*)

Welding

Part 2: '*Specification for symbols for welding*' of the British Standard, BS 499 was published in 1980 in a completely revised form. This revision brings the symbols to be used in drawings more in line with accepted international standard symbols.

The diagrams on this page showing methods of drawing welded joints and showing the symbols for the welds are all based on the recommendations of the revised British Standard. Only the more commonly used welds are shown on this page. Further information can be obtained by reference to BS 499: Part 2: 1980.

Each welded joint is shown by three drawings. The drawings on the left are views of the joints showing the actual shape of the welds. The centre drawings show how the joints should be drawn in end views. The drawings on the right show how the joints should be drawn in front views.

Note: The weld symbols are drawn with thick lines either under or across a thin horizontal reference line. The end of the reference line touches a thin arrow line, drawn at 60° and ending with an arrow touching the actual joint line.

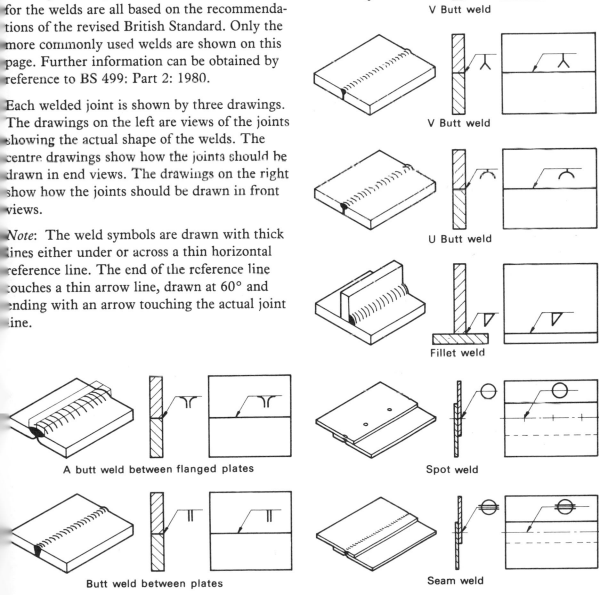

V Butt weld

V Butt weld

U Butt weld

Fillet weld

A butt weld between flanged plates

Spot weld

Butt weld between plates

Seam weld

Exercises

1   A pictorial view of a welded rocker base column is shown. Sketch a front elevation. (*City and Guilds*)

2   The drawing shows a pictorial sketch of a beam to column connection of welded construction. Sketch a front elevation in the direction of arrow A, an end elevation and a plan view. Indicate the welds in accordance with British Standards symbols. (*City and Guilds*)

3   The drawing gives details of a chain cover to be fabricated from low carbon steel sheet 1 mm thick and secured to a 6 mm vertical plate of a machine AB so that it may easily provide access.
(a) Draw to a scale of 1:5 the front and end elevations given and from them produce a plan.
(b) Indicate on the drawing THREE welding symbols for the joints to be used in fabrication. (*City and Guilds*)

4   The drawing shows the pictorial view of a cast iron bed plate for a machine. The casting is to be replaced by a welded construction. Using a scale of 1:10 draw a front elevation in the direction of the arrow A and project a plan view beneath. Use the following materials: do not dimension, but add weld symbols.

Materials list

1 off   480 × 100 R.S. Channel × 580 long
1 off   380 × 100 R.S. Channel × 480 long
1 off   300 × 100 R.S. Channel × 380 long
4 off   64 × 15 mounting pads × 300 long
(*City and Guilds*)

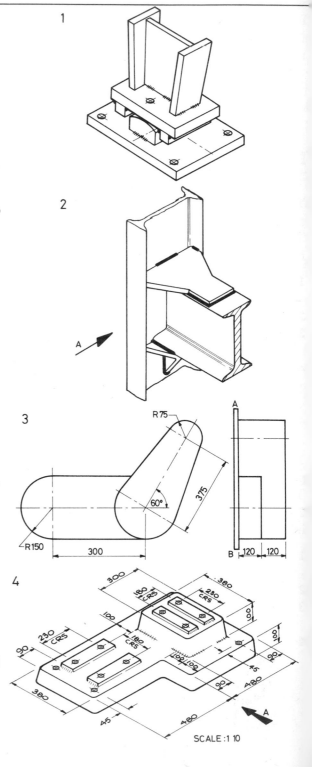

1

2

3

R75
R150   300   375   60°
A   B   120 120

4

300   380
180 CRS   280 CRS
100
230 CRS   180 CRS
90   100 100
380   45   480
45   480

SCALE : 1 10

4 True shapes

When developing patterns for sheet metal-working the *true shape* of a face will often have to be constructed. This can only be seen by looking directly at the face from a viewing position taken along lines at right angles to the face.

This means that the *first rule* to be observed, when constructing the true shape of a face, is that the face must be viewed at right angles.

Prisms

True shape of sloping face of a square prism
The prism has a square base 40 mm long and a height 65 mm with a sloping face at 45°.

1 Viewing direction is shown by arrow A at 90° to the sloping face.
2 Project lines at 90° to the sloping face.
3 Mark off the length a from the plan along one of the projected lines.
4 Complete the true shape by drawing lines parallel to the sloping face from the ends of line a.

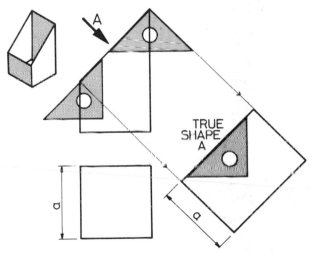

True shape of sloping face of a square prism

True shape of sloping face of a rectangular prism
The rectangle of the prism is 40 mm by 25 mm. Height of prism is 80 mm and the sloping face is at 60° to the horizontal.

1 Viewing direction is shown by arrow B at 90° to sloping face.
2 Project lines at 90° to the sloping face.
3 Mark off the length b from the plan along one of the projected lines.
4 Complete the true shape by drawing lines parallel to the sloping face from the ends of line b.

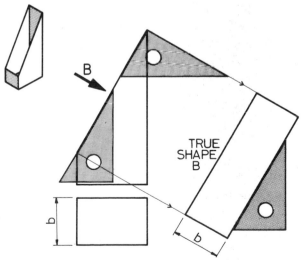

True shape of sloping face of a rectangular prism

True shape of sloping face of a triangular prism

The equilateral triangular prism has sides 35 mm long. Height is 40 mm and the sloping face is at 45° to the horizontal.

1   Viewing direction is shown by arrow C at 90° to slope of face.
2   Project lines at 90° to the sloping face.
3   Mark off the two lengths c, taken from the plan, along the projection line from the lower end of the front view.
4   Complete the true shape as shown. The central line to the apex of the triangle forming the true shape is parallel to the sloping face.

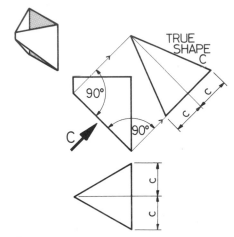

True shape of sloping face of a triangular prism

True shape of sloping face of a hexagonal prism

The sides of the hexagon are 20 mm long. The height of the prism is 75 mm and its sloping face is at 45° to the horizontal. Arrow of viewing D is at 90° to the sloping face.

1   Project lines at right angles to the sloping face.
2   Mark off along the lower of the three projection lines the distances a and b taken from the plan.
3   Complete the TRUE SHAPE D as shown.

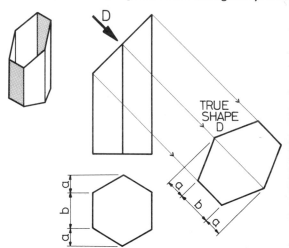

True shape of sloping face of a hexagonal prism

True shape of sloping face of a hexagonal prism

The sides of the hexagon are 20 mm long. Height of the prism is 30 mm and the slope of the face 30° to the horizontal. Arrow of viewing is F. Note the position of the true shape drawing in relation to the front view.

This example follows a procedure similar to that given for the example above.

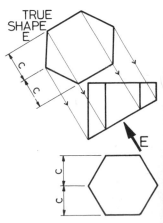

True shape of sloping face of a hexagonal prism

Pyramids

True shape of sloping face of a square pyramid

The base of the pyramid is a square of 40 mm sides. Height to apex is 60 mm. Highest point of sloping face is 40 mm above the base. The slope is at 45° to the horizontal. Viewing arrow F is at 90° to the sloping face.

1   Draw the front view and plan.
2   Project lines at 90° to the sloping face.
3   Draw a central line for the true shape drawing at right angles to these projection lines.
4   Mark off the lengths d and e, taken from the plan, each side of this central line.
5   Complete the TRUE SHAPE F drawing as shown.

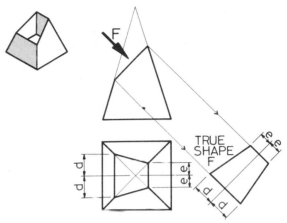

True shape of sloping face of a square pyramid

True shape of sloping face of a rectangular pyramid

The rectangular base is 55 mm by 20 mm, height 70 mm. Slope is at angle of 30° commencing 12 mm above base. Angle of viewing A is at 90° to the sloping face. Note the construction of the front view and plan.

1   Draw the plan of the pyramid before the slope face is cut.
2   Project the whole front view from the plan.
3   Draw the line of the sloping face on the front view.
4   Project the ends of the sloping face line into the plan.
5   Complete the plan as shown.

True shape of sloping face of a rectangular pyramid

To construct the TRUE SHAPE A
1   Project lines at right angles to the sloping face.
2   Draw a central line for the true shape drawing at right angles to these projection lines.
3   Mark off the lengths a and b each side of this central line. Lengths a and b are taken from the plan.
4   Complete the TRUE SHAPE A drawing as shown.

True shape of sloping face of a hexagonal pyramid

The hexagonal base has side lengths of 25 mm. Overall height of pyramid is 65 mm. The highest point of the sloping face is 35 mm and the slope is at 45°. Viewing arrow B is at 90° to the sloping face.

1 Project lines at 90° to the sloping face.
2 Draw the central line of the true shape drawing at right angles to the projection lines.
3 Mark off the lengths c, d and e, taken from the plan, along the projection lines, each side of the central line.
4 Complete the TRUE SHAPE B as shown.

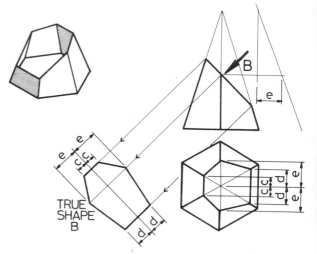

True shape of sloping face of a hexagonal pyramid

Cylinders

True shape of sloping face of a cylinder

The cylinder is of a diameter 40 mm and height 60 mm cut at 60° to the horizontal. Viewing arrow C is at 90° to the sloping face.

Stage 1

1 Divide the circle of the plan into twelve equal parts.
2 Project lines at right angles to the sloping face.
3 Draw a line at right angles to the projection lines to give a centre line for the true shape drawing. This centre line is parallel to the sloping face.

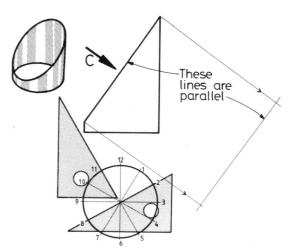

True shape of sloping face of a cylinder. Stage 1

Stage 2

Arrows on the projection lines show the direction in which they are projected.

4 Project lines from points 1 to 12 in the plan vertically upwards to the front view. It is advisable to *number* the points in the plan and the lines on the front view.
5 Where the numbered projected lines in the front view touch the sloping face, project lines at 90° to the sloping face across the true shape centre line.
6 Mark off the lengths a, b and c taken from the plan along the respective lines projected from the sloping face. These lengths must be taken *each* side of the central line.
7 Draw a fair freehand curve neatly through the twelve points so constructed to obtain the TRUE SHAPE C.
8 *Note*: the TRUE SHAPE C is an *ellipse*.

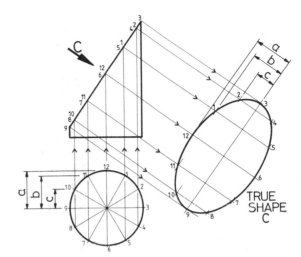

True shape of sloping face of a cylinder. Stage 2

Cones

True shape of sloping face of cone
The cone base is of diameter 80 mm and height 90 mm cut by a sloping face at 45° to give a maximum height of 60 mm.

Stage 1

1 Draw the front view and plan of the whole cone.
2 Mark three horizontal lines AA, BB and CC parallel to the base to cut the sloping face at 2, 3 and 4.
3 Project down into the plan the circles formed by the cuts made across the *whole* cone by lines AA, BB and CC.
4 At points 1, 2, 3, 4 and 5 in the front view project down to the plan on to the circles A, B and C and on to the plan centre line to give points 2, 3 and 4 each side of the centre line of the plan and 1 and 5 on the centre line.

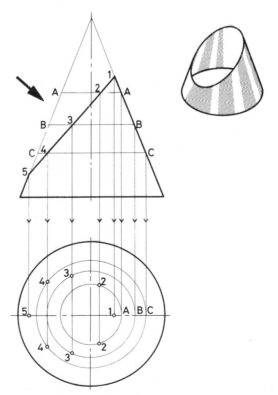

True shape of sloping face of a cone. Stage 1

Stage 2

5 At the points 1, 2, 3, 4 and 5 on the sloping face project lines at right angles to the slope.

6 Draw a line at right angles to these projection lines to give a central line for the true shape drawing.

7 Mark off the distances a, b and c taken from the plan to give the points numbered 1, 2, 3, 4 and 5 on the true shape drawing.

8 Draw a fair freehand curve through the numbered points to obtain the TRUE SHAPE A.

Note: The TRUE SHAPE A is an *ellipse*.

True shape of sloping face of a cone

The cone is of base diameter 60 mm and height 70 mm cut by a sloping face parallel to the slope line of the cone and 15 mm from the slope line. Viewing direction is from B, at right angles to the sloping face.

Follow the same procedure as for the two stages shown to obtain the TRUE SHAPE A in the cone above.

1 Draw three horizontal lines across the front view.

2 Project these lines into the plan and draw the circles they represent.

3 Where the horizontal lines across the front view intersect the sloping face, project down into the plan on to the respective circles.

4 Project lines at right angles from the slope face.

5 Draw a line at right angles to these projection lines to give a central line for the true shape drawing.

6 Mark off the lengths a, b, c and d, taken from the plan, each side of the central line.

7 Complete the true shape drawing by drawing a fair freehand curve through the plotted points.

Note: The TRUE SHAPE B is a curve known as a *parabola*.

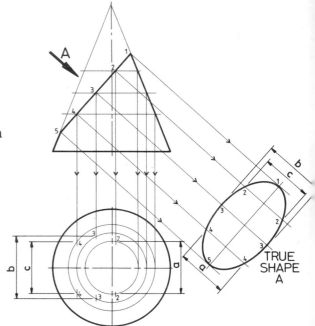

True shape of sloping face of a cone. Stage 2

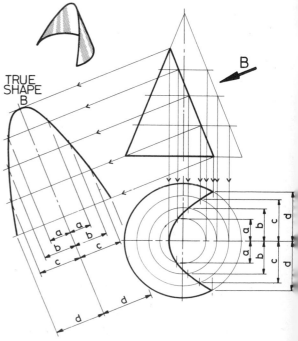

True shape of sloping face of a cone

True shape of a vertical face of a cone

The cone base is of diameter 74 mm and height 85 mm cut by a vertical face 15 mm from the axis of the cone. Viewing direction is arrow C at right angles to the face.

1 Draw three lines parallel to the base to cut the vertical face line.
2 Project these lines into the plan and draw the circles they represent.
3 Project the line of the vertical face into the plan. Widths for the true shape can then be taken at the points where the circles cross this line.
4 Project lines at right angles to the vertical face. Draw a central true shape line at 90° to these projection lines.
5 Mark off lengths a, b, c and d taken from the plan, each side of the true shape central line.
6 Draw a fair freehand curve through the plotted points to complete the TRUE SHAPE C.

Note: The TRUE SHAPE C curve is known as a *hyperbola*.

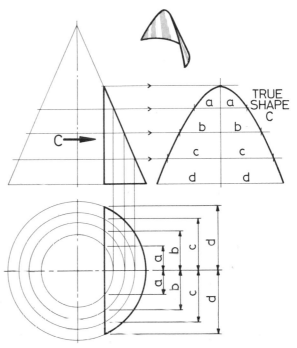

True shape of a vertical face of a cone

True shape of vertical face of an oblique cone

The cone is of base diameter 54 mm. The axis slopes at 60° to the base. The vertical height of the cone is 70 mm and the vertical face is taken 30 mm horizontally from the centre of the base. Viewing direction is shown by arrow D at 90° to the vertical face.

1 Draw three horizontal lines to cut across the vertical face in the front view.
2 Project and draw the circles represented by these lines in the plan.
3 Project the plan line of the vertical face into the plan.
4 Take the distances a and b from where the vertical face line in the plan cuts the plan circles.

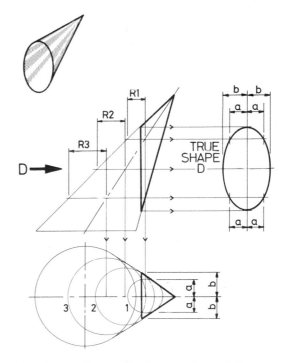

True shape of a vertical face of an oblique cone

5   Project lines at right angles to the vertical
face in the front view.
6   Draw a true shape central line at right
angles to these projected lines.
7   Mark off the distances a and b each side of
the true shape central line.
8   Draw a fair freehand curve through these
plotted points to obtain the TRUE SHAPE
D.

Note: The TRUE SHAPE D curve is an
ellipse.

True shape of sloping face of a cone: another method

A different method of constructing the true
shape of the sloping face of a cone is shown.
Compare this example with the examples given
on pages 41 and 42.

Cone base diameter is 82 mm and height is
95 mm, truncated at 45°. Lowest point of truncation is 26 mm above the base.

1   Divide the circle of the plan into twelve
equal parts. Join each of the points to the
apex in the plan.
2   Project the twelve points to the base line of
the front view. Join the points on the base to
the apex in the front view.
3   Where these sloping lines meet the truncation line in the front view, project lines at
right angles to the truncation line.
4   Draw a centre line for the true shape drawing at right angles to these projection lines.
5   From where the sloping lines in the front
view meet the truncation line, project down
into the plan.
6   The points at which these projection lines
meet the dividing lines in the plan are on
the ellipse of the truncated surface.
7   Draw this ellipse through the points in the
plan.
8   Measure the distances a, b, c, d and e in
the plan with a compass and mark each

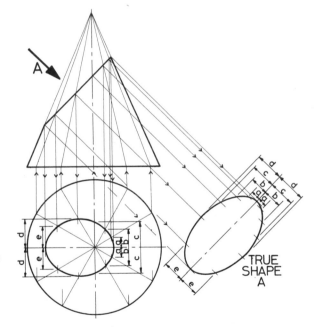

*True shape of sloping face of a cone: another
method*

distance in turn each side of the centre line
of the true shape drawing.
9   Draw a fair freehand curve through the
points obtained to complete the ellipse of
the TRUE SHAPE A.

True shape of sloping face of a cone

Cone base diameter is 82 mm and height 96 mm. The sloping face is parallel to the slant side of the cone and commencing 15 mm in from base.

The construction shown in this example follows the same procedure as given for the example above.

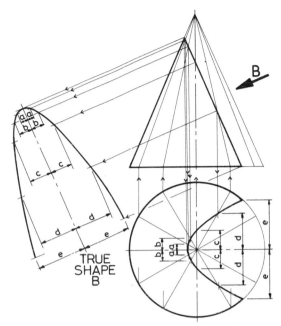

True shape of sloping face of a cone

True shape of vertical face of cone

Cone base diameter is 70 mm and height 90 mm. The vertical face is 12 mm from the vertical axis.

This example follows the construction procedure already given on page 44.

1 From point 1 on the plan project to 2 on the front view and to 4 on the end view.
2 Join points 1, 2 and 4 to the apex in each view.
3 From A in the plan, project to B in the front view.
4 From B project to C — a point on the curve of the TRUE SHAPE C.
5 Repeat this process for other points on the true shape curve.

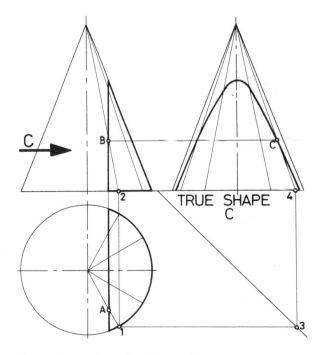

True shape of vertical face of a cone

True shape of vertical face of oblique cone

Cone base diameter is 70 mm and vertical height 90 mm. The axis is at 50° to the base. The vertical plane is as shown. This example again follows the construction procedure given on page 44.

Note: The construction used to obtain the true shape of a face of a right cone cut by a plane can be followed when constructing a true shape for a face of an oblique cone cut by a plane.

1   From 1 in the plan project to 2 in the front view and 4 in the end view.
2   Join points 1 and 4 to the apex in all three views.
3   A in the plan is represented by B in the front view — A and B are on the same line to the apex.
4   Project point B into the end view to give C.
5   Repeat for all twelve division lines to obtain sufficient points in the end view in order to draw a fair freehand curve to give the TRUE SHAPE D.

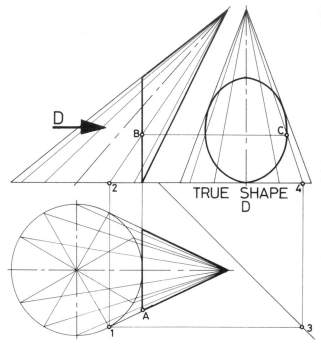

True shape of vertical face of oblique cone

Worked examples

Four worked examples of true shape constructions are shown.

1   Find the true shape of the hole to be cut in the sloping sheet AB to take the hexagonal pipe.

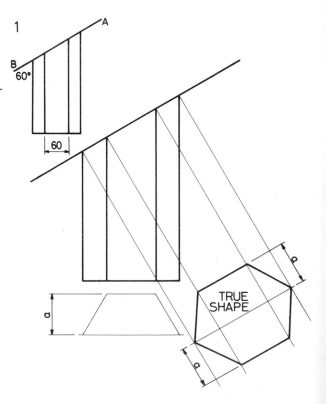

2 Find the true shape of the base of the hopper.

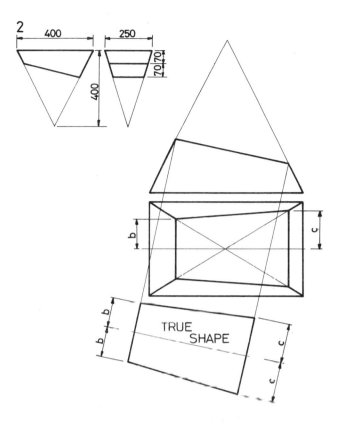

3 Find the true shape of the hole to be cut in the vertical sheet **AB** to receive the conical spout.

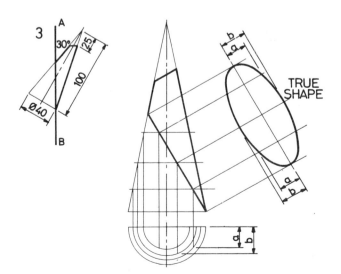

4   Find the true shape of the joint line AB between the two parts of the breeches piece.

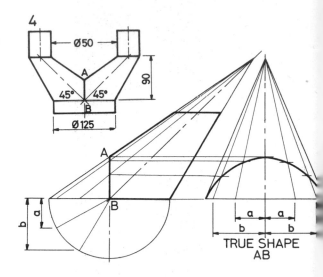

TRUE SHAPE
AB

Exercises

The reader is advised to copy the drawings for exercises 1, 2 and 3 to a scale of 1:1 before drawing the solutions to the questions.

1   A rectangular plate X–X is to be welded on to a right cylinder as shown. Draw the true shape of the hole to be cut in the plate. (*City and Guilds*)

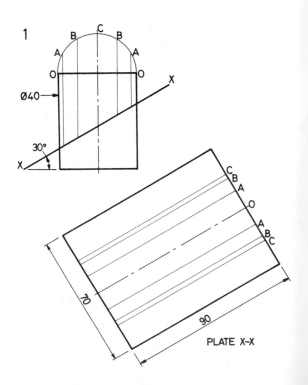

PLATE X–X

2 Draw the true shape of the hole to be cut in the flat plate AB in order to accommodate the pouring spout shown. (*City and Guilds*)

2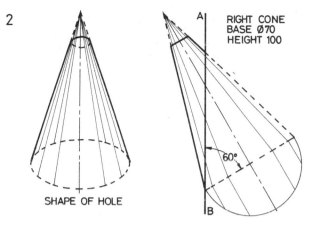

RIGHT CONE
BASE Ø70
HEIGHT 100

SHAPE OF HOLE

60°

3 Complete the true shape of the cutting plane X–X on the lines given. (*City and Guilds*)

3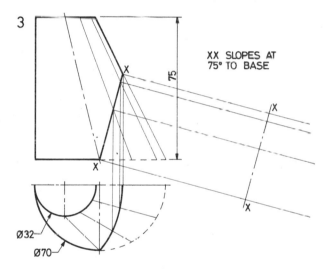

XX SLOPES AT
75° TO BASE

Ø32

Ø70

4 A hopper fitted with a chute is shown. Using a scale of 1:5:
(a) draw the views given showing the intersection line between the hopper and the chute in the plan view (see pages 53 to 72);
(b) develop a pattern for the plate marked A showing the true shape of the hole required for fitting the chute (see pages 82 to 84). (*City and Guilds*)

Work to a scale of 1:1 (full size) when constructing the solutions to exercises 5 to 21.

4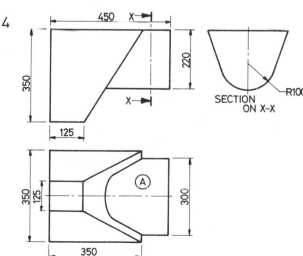

450

220

350

125

SECTION
ON X–X

R100

350

125

300

350

(A)

5–13 The drawings numbered 5 to 13 are two-view orthographic projections each comprising a front view and a plan. The drawings are on a 20 mm square grid, each square on the grid having sides of 20 mm length. Dimensions for each of the drawings are obtained by counting along the 20 mm lengths. Thus drawing 5 shows a front view and a plan of a square prism of sides 80 mm long, of height 100 mm with a sloping face at 45°.

Construct the true shape of the sloping faces of each of the shapes shown in drawings 5 to 13. Name the geometrical forms shown by each of these drawings.

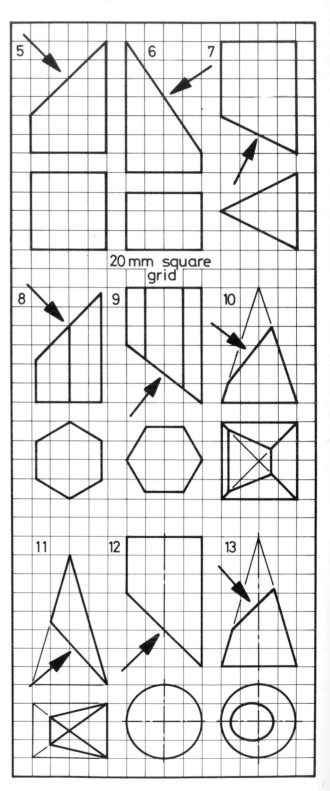

20 mm square grid

14–19 The drawings 14 to 19 show front views and plans of right and oblique cones cut by sloping and vertical faces. Construct the true shapes as seen in the directions of the arrows of each of the faces of the cones shown in drawings 14 to 19.

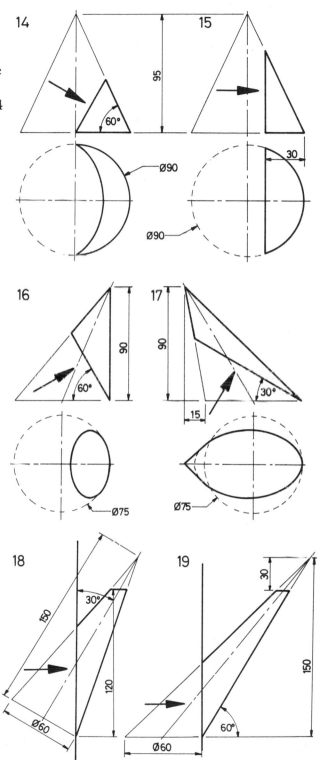

20   A front view of a two-way branch pipe is shown. Construct the true shape of the joint line AB between the two parts of the branch pipe.

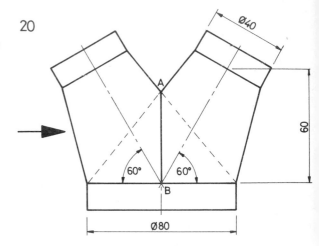

21   A front view of a two-way branch pipe is shown. Construct the true shape of the joint line CD between the two parts of the branch pipe.

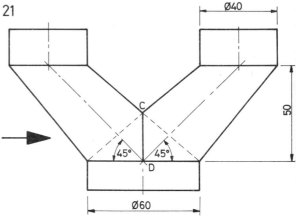

Two equal diameter tubes forming a 120° cylindrical elbow

5 Lines of intersection

Between parts of equal section

Eight examples of lines of intersection between parts of equal section are shown on this page and pages 54 and 55. Note that in all these examples the line of intersection as seen in the front views is either a straight line or is made up of several straight lines.

Drawing 1

This shows a 90° corner joint between two equal square tubes. A front view and end view are shown. The joint line LL is a straight line and is at 45° to each of the square tubes.

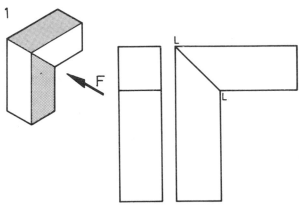

Front view and end view of 90° joint between equal square tubes

Drawing 2

A front view and an end view of a 90° corner joint between two equal cylindrical tubes is shown. Again, in the front view, the joint line LL is straight and forms an angle of 45° with each of the cylindrical tubes.

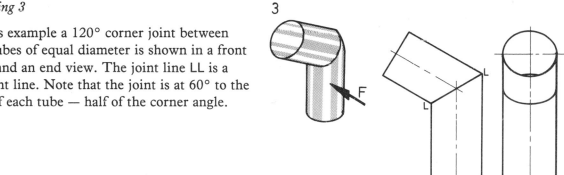

Front view and end view of 90° joint between equal cylindrical tubes

Drawing 3

In this example a 120° corner joint between two tubes of equal diameter is shown in a front view and an end view. The joint line LL is a straight line. Note that the joint is at 60° to the axis of each tube — half of the corner angle.

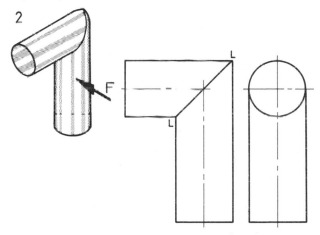

Front view and end view of 120° joint between equal cylindrical tubes

Drawing 4

This shows a 90° Tee joint between two equal rectangular tubes. The joint line LLL in the front view consists of two straight lines each at 45° to the upright face of one of the tubes.

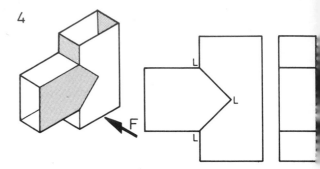

Front view and end view of 90° Tee joint between equal rectangular tubes

Drawing 5

A 90° Tee joint between equal cylindrical tubes is shown. Note the similarity between the joint line in the front view of this example to that of drawing 4. Again the joint line LLL is composed of two straight lines.

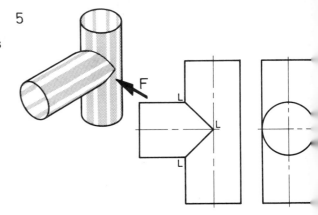

Front view and end view of 90° Tee joint between equal cylindrical tubes

Drawing 6

This shows in front view and end view a 60° joint between two cylinders of equal diameter. The joint line LLL as seen in the front view is two straight lines forming an angle at the point where the two centre lines of the cylinders meet.

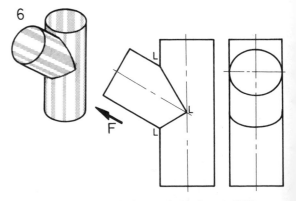

Front view and end view of a joint at 60° between cylinders of equal diameter

Drawing 7

Two hexagonal tubes meeting at an angle of 60° are shown. Again, the joint line is composed of two straight lines forming an angle at the point where the central lines of the hexagonal tubes meet.

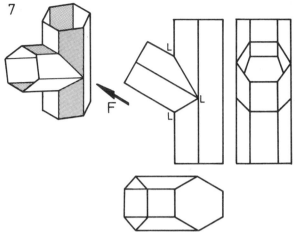

Front view, end view and plan of a joint at 60° between equal hexagonal tubes

Drawing 8

This is another drawing showing a 60° joint between hexagonal tubes, but this time with the hexagonal faces positioned differently to those in drawing 7. The joint line LLLL is made up of three straight lines.

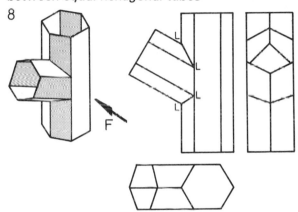

Front view, end view and plan of a joint at 60° between equal hexagonal tubes

Between parts of unequal section

The joint lines of parts of unequal section show as straight lines if both parts forming the joint are of sections with flat sides. Seven examples of such joint lines are given on this page and on pages 56 and 57.

Drawing 1

This shows lines of intersection between two square tubes forming a 90° Tee joint. A tube of 16 mm sides is jointed to one of 24 mm sides. The line of intersection shown on the front view consists of two straight lines.

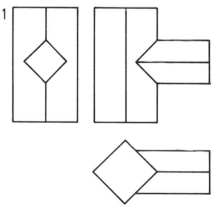

Front view, end view and plan of joint of unequal square tubes

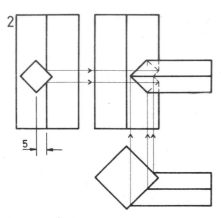

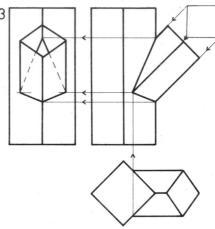

Front view, end view and plan of joint of unequal square tubes

Front view, end view and plan of a joint at 60° between square tubes of unequal size

Drawing 2

A square tube of 12 mm sides is joined off-centre at 90° to a square tube of 22 mm sides. The following drawing procedure should be followed:

1   Draw the plan.
2   Draw the end view.
3   Project from plan and end view to construct the front view.

Note the hidden detail of the joint line in the front view.

Drawing 3

A square tube of 18 mm sides is joined at an angle of 45° to a square tube of 24 mm sides.

The following drawing procedure should be followed:

1   Draw the plan of the tube of 24 mm sides.
2   Project a front view from the plan.
3   Draw the central line of the 45° angle of the 18 mm tube.
4   In line with the 45° line draw the true shape of the square of the 18 mm tube.
5   Project its edges back into the front view and complete the front view.
6   Now project to and complete the plan and end view.

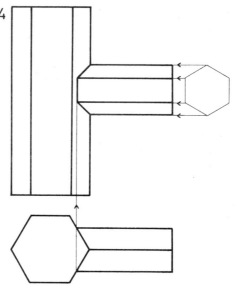

Front view and plan of joint between unequal hexagonal tubes

Drawing 4

A tube of hexagonal section of edge lengths 14 mm is joined at right angles to a hexagonal tube of 20 mm edge lengths.

In order to draw the three views follow a similar procedure as for drawing 3 in that the true shape of the 14 mm sided tube must be drawn in line with the angle at which it is jointed to the larger tube.

Drawing 5

A tube of hexagonal section of sides 14 mm long is joined at right angles to a hexagonal tube of 18 mm side length.

Again follow the procedure as for drawing 4. Note the vertical lines on the true shape construction for the hexagon of the smaller tube. These are 18 mm apart to indicate the position where the smaller tube enters the flat side of the larger tube.

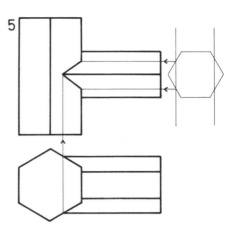

Front view and plan of joint between unequal hexagonal tubes

Drawing 6

A hexagonal tube of 13 mm edge lengths is joined to a hexagonal tube of 18 mm edge lengths at an angle of 90° with the front edges of both tubes in the same plane.

Again the true shape of the smaller tube is required in order to complete the front view and construct the joint line.

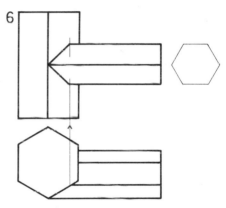

Front view and plan of joint between unequal hexagonal tubes

Drawing 7

A square tube of 14 mm edges is joined at 60° to a hexagonal tube of 24 mm edges.

To draw a front view and a plan of this assembly:

1 Draw the outline of the plan of the hexagonal tube.
2 Draw the front view of the hexagonal tube.
3 Draw the central line of the square tube at 60° to the hexagonal tube in the front view.
4 Draw the true shape of the square tube projected along the 60° line.
5 Draw the other corners of the square tube in the front view and project its shape into the plan.
6 From where the square tube in the plan meets the sides of the hexagon project up into the front view to obtain the line of intersection. Note that the hidden detail is included.

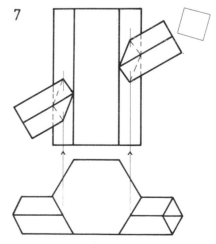

Front view and plan of joint at 60° between a square tube and a hexagonal tube

The common central sphere

If, at the area of an intersection between cylinders and cones, or between cones, a *sphere* can be exactly fitted inside the parts forming the intersection, then the joint lines, as seen from the front, will show as *straight lines*.

This is the principle of the *common central sphere*. Ten examples of the application of this principle are shown in drawings on this page and on pages 59 and 60. In each of the ten examples given, the common central sphere is shown by a circle.

Drawings 1 to 5 include a pictorial drawing of the intersecting parts. Drawings 6 to 10 show the necessary constructions to determine the positions of the straight lines of the intersections in the front views. The reader is advised to construct the intersections shown in drawings 6 to 10 to the dimensions given.

Drawing 1

A right cone joined to a cylinder so that the cylinder axis and the cone axis meet at right angles. The centre of the common central sphere is at the intersection of the two axes.

Drawing 2

This shows a right cone joined to a cylinder with the axes of the two shapes meeting at right angles. The common central sphere centre is at the intersection of the two axes.

Drawing 3

A right cone joined to a cylinder with the axes of the two parts forming an angle of 120° is shown. The centre of the common central sphere is at the intersection of the two axes.

1

Joint between cone and cylinder

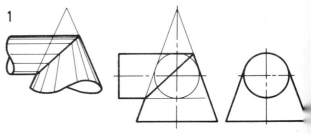

2

Joint between cone and cylinder

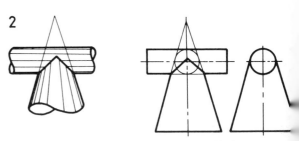

3

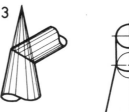

Joint between cone and cylinder

Drawing 4

This shows a right cone intersected by a cylinder with their axes at 60° to each other. The axes intersect at the centre of the common central sphere.

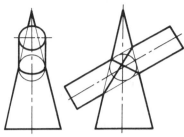

Joint between cone and cylinder

Drawing 5

A cone joined to a cylinder is shown with axes at right angles. There is a common central sphere centred at the intersection of the axes.

In diagrams 5 to 10 the left-hand drawing shows the construction, the right-hand drawing is a front view.

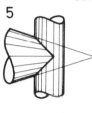
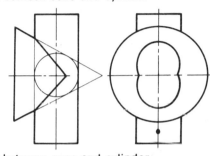

Joint between cone and cylinder

Drawing 6

This shows a larger cone with a base diameter of 40 mm and a common central sphere of diameter 20 mm. The centre of the common central sphere is 32 mm above the base of the larger cone and the angle of axes is 150°. The small cone base diameter is 30 mm and the centre of the sphere is 18 mm from the base of the smaller cone. The line of intersection is LL.

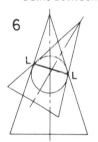

Joint between two right cones

Drawing 7

The cylinder diameter is 28 mm and cone base diameter 40 mm with axes at right angles. The line of intersection is LL.

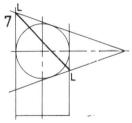
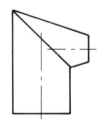

Joint between a cylinder and a cone

Drawing 8

The cylinder diameter is 28 mm.
Cones — diameters at cylinder centre line are 32 mm.

Note that the intersection is made up of three straight lines, L_1L_1; L_2L_2; L_3. (L_3 is on the centre line of the cylinder.)

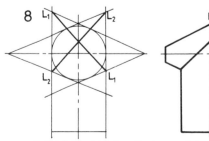

Joint between a cylinder and two cones

Drawing 9

The cone base diameter is 48 mm and the cylinder diameters 20 mm. One cylinder axis meets cone axis at 90°; the second cylinder axis meets cone axis at 110°.

Note that the intersection is made up of three straight lines, L_1L_1; L_2L_2; L_3. (L_3 is a radius of the common central sphere.)

Drawing 10

Cone base diameter is 50 mm and cylinder diameter 30 mm. The cone is inclined at 80° to the cylinder. Line of intersection is LL.

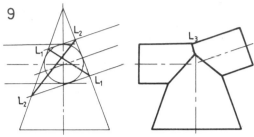

Joint between a cone and two cylinders

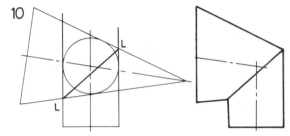

Joint between a cone and a cylinder

Curves of intersection

If two cylinders of unequal diameter intersect, the line of intersection as seen in a front view will be a *curve*.

The principle on which such *curves of intersection* are constructed is based on the method of taking a number of parallel sectional cuts across both intersecting parts. Each sectional cut will show up points where the two parts meet each other. Drawings 1, 2 and 3 show how the sectional cuts enable a curve of intersection to be plotted and drawn. Each of the drawings 1, 2 and 3 includes a pictorial drawing and an orthographic three-view projection of the resulting construction. Drawing 4 is a completed drawing including the curve of intersection plotted by this method of parallel sectional cuts. The construction lines to obtain the curve have been left on drawing 4 to show the method as applied to a drawing.

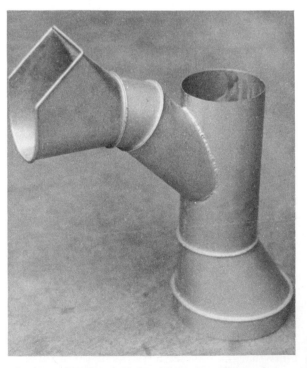

A shute leading to joins between pipes of unequal diameter

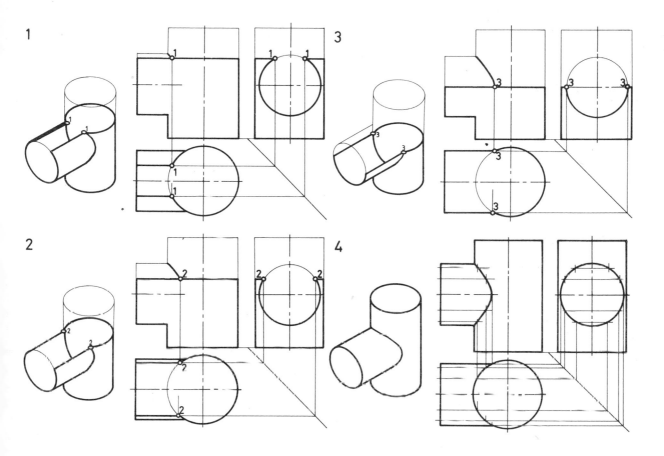

Intersection between cylinders meeting at 90°

Drawing 1

To construct the curve of intersection between two cylinders, one of diameter 56 mm, the second of diameter 40 mm, meeting at right angles with their axes offset by 6 mm:

1 Draw the plan of the two cylinders.
2 Project from the plan to the front view of the larger cylinder and insert the lines showing the diameter of the smaller cylinder. Draw both centre lines.
3 In projection with the front view of the smaller cylinder draw the circle of its end view.
4 Divide this circle into twelve equal parts to give points 1–12.

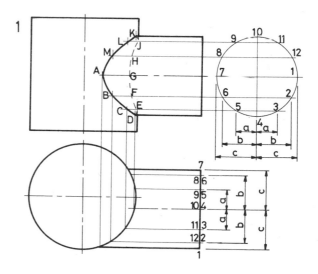

5 Project points 1– 12 across the front view.

6 Take the distances a, b and c on the end view circle and transfer them to the plan. Note the positions of the numbered points in this plan construction.

7 At the points where the lines of width a, b and c in the plan meet the larger cylinder, project upwards into the front view to meet the lines drawn across the front view to give points A, B to M.

8 Join these lettered points with a fair freehand curve to obtain the required curve of intersection.

Note that the hidden detail of the rear part of the curve of intersection is required.

Drawing 2

To construct the curve of intersection between two cylinders, one of diameter 56 mm, the second of diameter 22 mm, with their fronts meeting along the same plane.

The procedure for constructing this line of intersection is similar to that given for constructing the line of intersection in drawing 1.

Drawing 3

To construct the lines of intersection between two pipes of diameters 26 mm and 42 mm meeting a pipe of diameter 62 mm in the positions as shown by the drawing. The centre lines of the 26 mm pipe and 62 mm pipe are offset by 6 mm.

The method of constructing the required curves of intersection is again the same as that given for drawing 1.

Note the method of drawing a semicircle at the ends of the two smaller pipes to obtain the required twelve divisions of each of the cylinders of the pipes. Note also the numbering of the divisions of these semicircles in the plan as compared with the numbering in the front view.

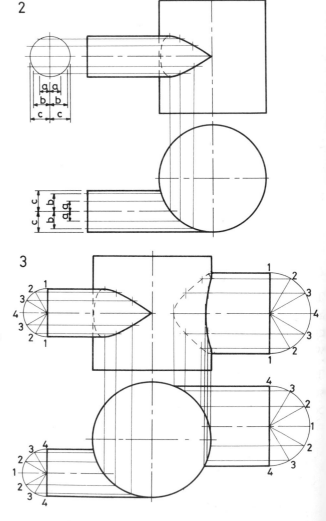

Intersection between cylinders meeting at angles other than 90°

Drawing 1

To construct the curve of intersection between a cylinder of diameter 40 mm meeting a cylinder of diameter 50 mm at an angle of 60°:

1 Draw the plan of the two cylinders. In order to draw the required curve of intersection *there is no need to draw the ellipse* in the plan showing the end of the smaller cylinder.
2 Project the outlines of the two cylinders into the front view. Draw their centre lines.
3 Draw a semicircle on the end of the front view of the smaller cylinder and divide it into six equal parts.
4 Draw lines through the points 2 to 6 parallel with the 60° centre line.
5 Draw the same half-circle in the plan centred on a projection of the centre line.
6 Project the points 2 to 6 in the plan parallel to the centre line to meet the larger cylinder circle.
7 Where lines 2 to 6 meet the plan, circle project into the front view to give the points B, C, D, E and F.
8 Draw a fair freehand curve through these lettered points to obtain the required curve of intersection.

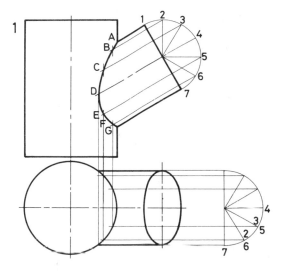

Drawing 2

To construct the curve of intersection between a cylinder of diameter 40 mm meeting a cylinder of diameter 50 mm at an angle of 45° with their fronts in the same vertical plane.

The method of constructing this curve of intersection is similar to that given for the construction shown in drawing 1.

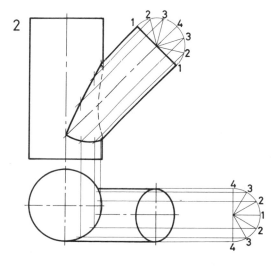

Drawing 3

To construct the curve of intersection between two pipes of square section, one of side lengths 30 mm, the second of side lengths 25 mm meeting at an angle of 60° and 90° respectively, a pipe of diameter 45 mm.

This construction follows a procedure similar to that given for the examples shown above. Note the following differences:

1 Half of the square section of the pipes is drawn in line with each pipe;
2 The lines numbered 1, 2, 3 and 4 can be drawn in any suitable position on the front view.

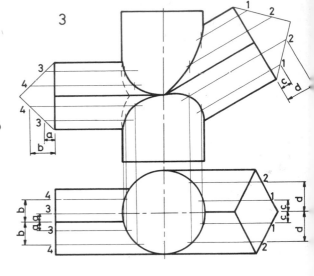

Curve of intersection between cylinder and right cone

Method 1

Four sectional cuts have been made horizontally across the cylinder and cone. Points on one of these four cuts have been marked 1 to 6. Follow the procedure shown by the points 1 to 6.

1 The cutting plane cuts the cylinder of the end view at 1 and the slope line of the front view at 2.
2 Project 2 on to the centre line of the plan giving 3.
3 With centre A and radius A3 draw a circle.
4 Draw a semicircle of cylinder radius on a projection of the centre line of the plan.
5 Measure the distance a in the end view with a compass and mark this distance a on the semicircle to give point 4.
6 Project point 4 on to circle A3 to give point 5. Point 5 is on the curve of intersection in the plan.
7 Project point 5 back to the line through 1 and 2 in the front view to give 6.
8 The point obtained — 6 — is on the curve of intersection in the front view.

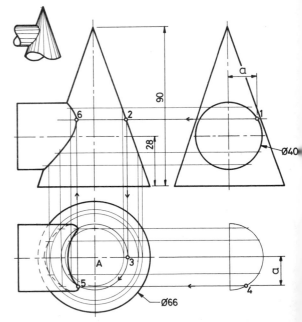

Curve of intersection between cylinder and right cone. Method 1

9 Draw fair freehand curves through all points so obtained.

Method 2

1 Divide plan circle into twelve equal parts. Join to apex.
2 Project points on plan circle to front and end views. Join to the apex in both views.
3 Point A is one of the twelve points on the end view.
4 Project A to B and B to C to obtain one point on the curve of intersection in both front view and plan.
5 Point 1 is one of the twelve points on the end view.
6 Project 1 to 2 and 2 to 3 to obtain a second point on the curve of intersection in both front view and plan.
7 Join the points so obtained with fair free-hand curves to complete the lines of intersection.

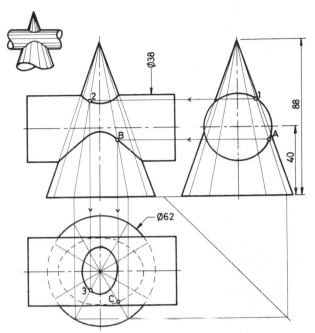

Curve of intersection between cylinder and right cone. Method 2

Oblique cones

Curve of intersection between cylinder and oblique cone

To construct the curve of intersection between the cylinder and the cone.

Note: This construction follows the procedure already shown by Method 2 above. In this example, however, the circle of the plan is not divided into twelve equal parts but divided so as to give usable points on the curve of intersection.

1 Take *any* point 1 on the end view. Join 1V.
2 Project 1 to 3 on the plan. Join 3V.
3 Project 3 to 4 in the front view. Join 4V.
4 At A on 1V, project to B on 4V and C on 3V.
5 Points B and C are on the required curves of intersection.

Note: T on the end view is a tangential point. It is necessary to draw the tangential line VT, and the point T must be projected to find the curve of intersection.

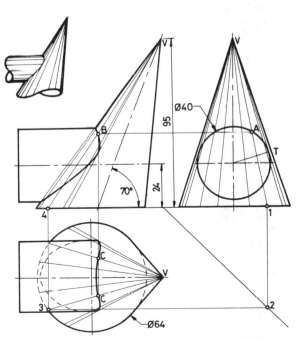

Curve of intersection between cylinder and oblique cone

Curve of intersection between square pipe and oblique cone

This is a pipe of square section of sides 30 mm meeting an oblique cone of base diameter 64 mm and height 90 mm with axis sloping at 70 mm to its base. Axes of pipe and cone meet 26 mm above base of cone.

Note: This construction follows the procedure already shown for Method 1 on page 64.

1 Take any horizontal cutting plane cutting at point 1 in the end view.
2 The plane cuts the axis of the cone in the front view at 2 and the slope line at 3.
3 Project 2 into the plan to give 4 and 3 into the plan to give 5.
4 Draw a circle centred at 4 and of radius 4–5.
5 Project point 1 from the end view to 7 on the circle 4–5.
6 Point 7 is a point on the curve of intersection in the plan.
7 Project 7 up to the front view to give point 8 on the cutting plane line through point 1.
8 Point 8 is a point on the curve of intersection in the front view.
9 Plot other points in the same way and draw fair freehand curves through such points to obtain the required curve of intersection.

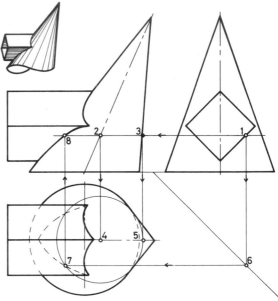

Curve of intersection between square pipe and an oblique cone

Sections taken across a sphere

If a flat sectional plane cuts across a sphere the resulting true shape outline is *always* a circle. The drawing shows three section planes A–A, B–B and C–C cutting a sphere at different angles and positions. The resulting true shapes AA, BB and CC are all circles. This principle is applied to the construction of lines of intersection between parts involving spheres.

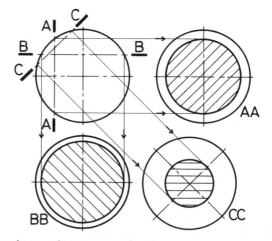

Sections taken across a sphere

Drawing 1

To construct the curves of intersection between a pipe of diameter 30 mm and a hemisphere of diameter 80 mm.

Note: In this example a cutting plane numbered 1 has been taken *vertically*. Only the *one* cutting plane has been drawn to avoid complicating the given drawing. In order to construct the required curve of intersection, *two* or *three* further cutting planes would be needed.

1   Draw a plan, front view and end view of the pipe and hemisphere without the lines of intersection.
2   Draw several cutting planes such as that numbered 1 parallel to each other.
3   At the point where the cutting plane meets the hemisphere at 2, project to the end view centre line to give 3 and draw the semicircle representing the section cut by line 1. This semicircle is of radius O3.
4   Where the semicircle meets the circle of the pipe — point 4 — this is a point on the intersection between the pipe and hemisphere.

5   Project point 4 to line 1 in the front view to give point 5.
6   Project point 4 to line 1 to give point 6 in the plan.
7   If several other vertical cutting planes are taken parallel to line 1, other points on the curves of intersection in the front view and plan can be constructed.
8   Draw fair freehand curves through the points to obtain the curves of intersection.

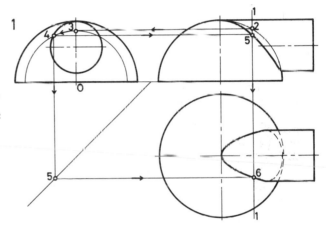

Drawing 2

A pipe of diameter 38 mm intersects a hemisphere of diameter 66 mm with the axes of the two parts offset by 10 mm.

To construct the curves of intersection in the front and end views, follow a procedure similar to that given for drawing 1, except that, in this example, section plane cuts are best taken horizontally.

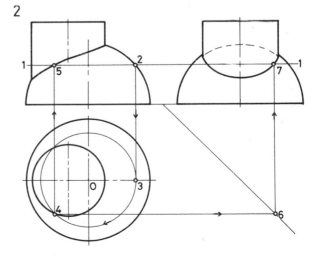

Exercises

The reader is advised to copy the given drawings for Exercises 1 to 9 to a scale of 1:1 (full size) before working the solutions.

1   Complete the line of intersection on the elevation given of the equal diameter branch pipe and the true shape of the hole to be cut in the horizontal pipe before rolling. (See pages 37 to 52 for a description of the true shapes of holes.) (*City and Guilds*)

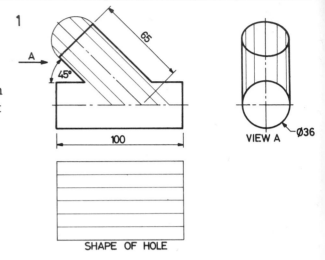

2   The drawing shows a front and an end elevation of a right cone intersected by a horizontal cylinder. Using the construction lines, complete the line of intersection on the elevation. (*City and Guilds*)

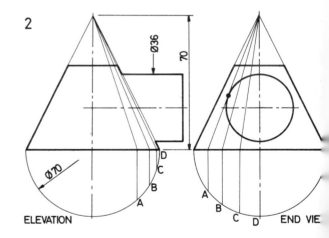

3   The drawing shows the elevation and projected view of a right cylinder joining a rectangular duct. Complete the curve of intersection in the given elevation. (*City and Guilds*)

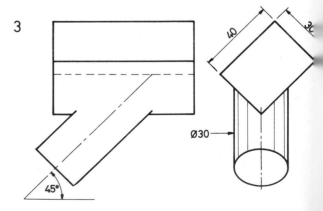

4 Complete the intersection in the front view for the cylindrical branch pipe shown. Hidden parts of the intersection should be shown. (*City and Guilds*)

4

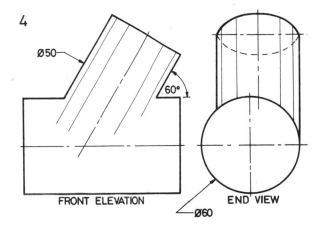

5 The drawing shows three existing tubes which are to be joined by a fabricated connecting piece comprising a part right cylinder and two part right cones. Using the principle of the common central sphere, complete the connection to show the joint lines between the pieces. (*City and Guilds*)

5

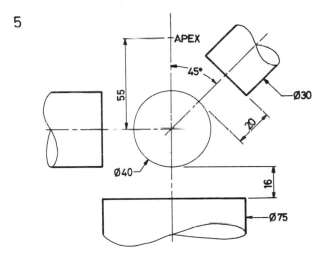

6 The drawing shows the outline of a hemisphere intersected by a vertical cylinder. Use the cutting planes given to draw the line of intersection on the elevation. (*City and Guilds*)

6

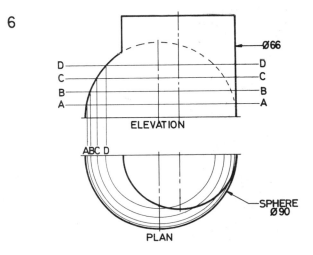

7 The drawing shows the plan and incomplete elevation of a square duct intersecting a right cone. Using the method of cutting planes, complete the partly drawn curve of intersection in the elevation. (*City and Guilds*)

7

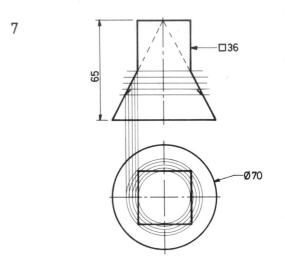

8 The drawing shows one half of a right cone frustum intersected by a horizontal cylinder. Using the cutting planes shown, complete the curve of intersection in both the plan and elevation. (*City and Guilds*)

8

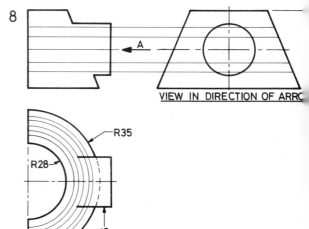

9 The drawing gives details of a right conical chute fitted to an inclined cylindrical delivery pipe.
(a) Draw the front elevation and VIEW A given and from them determine the line of intersection. Scale 1:10.
(b) Develop a half pattern for the conical chute. (See pages 110 and 111 for a description of the development of part (b)). (*City and Guilds*)

9

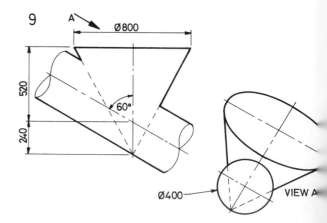

Curves of intersection between a cone and a hemisphere

The two drawings on this page and page 72 are examples of the methods of constructing the curves of intersection between a cone and a hemisphere.

Drawing 1

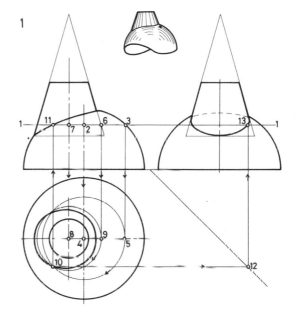

To construct the curve of intersection between a right cone of base diameter 44 mm and height 75 mm and a hemisphere of diameter 76 mm with their centres offset by 10 mm.

1   Draw the front view, end view and plan of the outline of the two parts, without their curves of intersection.
2   Draw several cutting planes across front and end views. Note that only one cutting plane numbered 1 is shown but at least *three* should be drawn.
3   The cutting plane 1 meets the centre line of the hemisphere in the front view at 2 and the circumference of the hemisphere at 3. Project 2 and 3 on to the plan centre line to obtain points 4 and 5.
4   With centre 4 draw circle of radius 4–5.
5   The cutting plane 1 meets the cone at 6 and the cone centre line at 7. Project these two points on to the centre line of the plan to give 8 and 9.
6   Draw a circle of centre 8 and radius 8–9.
7   Where circle centre 4 meets circle centre 8 is point 10. Point 10 is a point on the curve of intersection in the plan.
8   Project point 10 up to line 1 in the front view to give point 11, which is on the curve of intersection in the front view.
9   Project point 10 to line 1 in the end view to give point 13, which is on the curve of intersection in the end view.
10 Repeat the above with, say, two more horizontal cutting planes to obtain sufficient points on the curves of intersection in all three views.

Drawing 2

An oblique cone of base diameter 46 mm and height 40 mm with its oblique axis at 60° to its base intersects a hemisphere of diameter 76 mm. The apex of the cone and the centre of the hemisphere are at the same point.

To construct the curves of intersection in the three views of this example follow the description of the construction given for drawing 1.

Note: In both drawings, arrows on the projection lines between views indicate the direction in which the projection should be made.

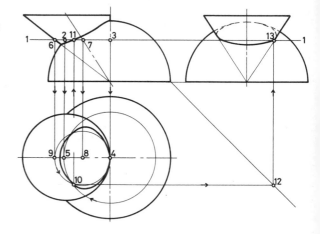

6 Parallel line development

In order to provide the patterns from which the developments of sheet metal articles can be made, three main methods of construction may be involved. These are:

Parallel line development;
Radial line development;
Development by triangulation.

This section of the book deals with methods of *parallel line development,* so called because the constructions for this form of development depend upon measurements and projections taken on and to parallel lines.

Examples of typical developments constructed on the principles of parallel line development are shown by the huge numbers of cardboard boxes and cartons used in packaging all types of goods. The illustration shows such a carton, together with a second illustration showing the carton opened out to show its development.

Note: The various tabs and flaps for gluing together the parts of the cardboard packet shown are not included in any of the constructions given in this book. This is because the methods of constructing sheet metal articles can vary considerably, examples being folding, soldering and welding. Joints at edges, corners and joins may or may not require tabs, seams and flaps, depending on the methods of jointing involved.

A typical food packet which will require a development

The pattern formed by opening out the food packet

The drawing shows the pattern of the development for a simple box in the form of a rectangular prism.

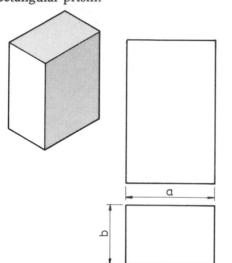

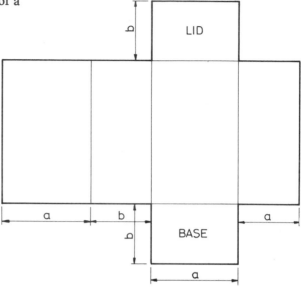

Box — truncated rectangular prism

A pictorial drawing of a box in the form of a truncated rectangular prism is shown. The sizes of the box are: rectangle 45 mm by 25 mm; overall height 70 mm; truncation at 45°.

To develop a pattern for the sides, top and bottom of the box

1 Draw a front view and a plan of the box.
2 Project lines parallel to the base from the corners of the front view.
3 Mark off along the base line the lengths AB, BC, CD and DA.

4 Draw verticals at A, B, C, D and A to meet the parallel lines from the front view.
5 Complete the development of the sides as shown.
6 The lid, a rectangle of width BC, and a base, a rectangle also of width BC, can now be added.

Note that an alternative method of constructing the development for the lid would be by drawing its true shape. This alternative is shown in a chain line drawing.

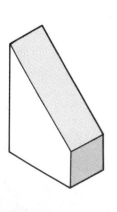

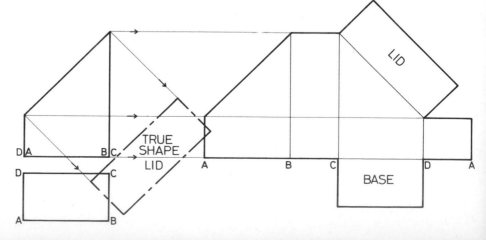

Three square tubes

A pictorial drawing of three square tubes meeting at right angles to form two corners is shown. The tubes are of 30 mm side lengths. The part B is 80 mm long.

To develop a pattern for the tube marked B:

1 Draw a front view and plan.
2 Project lines parallel to the base from the corners of the front view.
3 Mark off along the base line four equal lengths AB, each 30 mm long.
4 Draw verticals from these points to meet the parallel lines from the front view.
5 Complete the development of part B as shown.

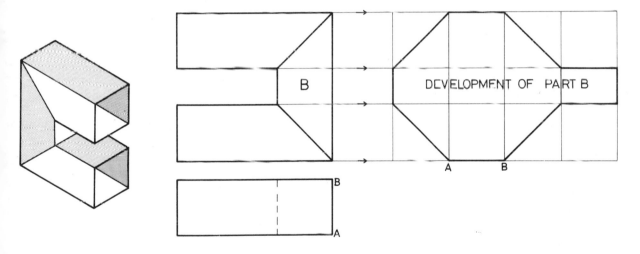

Development of truncated hexagonal prism

The sides of the hexagon are each 25 mm long. The overall vertical height of the prism is 65 mm. The truncation is at 60° to the highest vertical edge.

To develop the sides of a truncated hexagonal prism:

1 Draw a front view and plan of the prism.
2 Project lines parallel to the base from all corners in the front view.
3 Mark off along the base line six spaces each the length of the hexagon side — 25 mm long.
4 From the points 1 to 6 to 1 along the base line, draw verticals to meet the parallel lines.
5 Complete the development as shown.

Note: If a lid for the prism was required, its development can be obtained by constructing its true shape, shown by a chain line drawing.

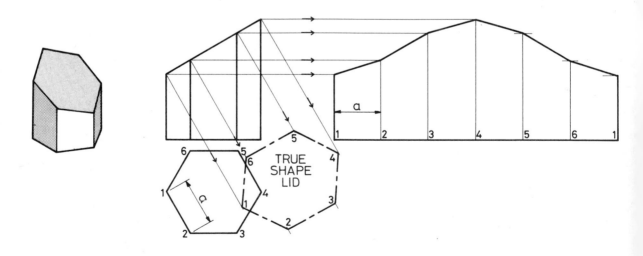

Development of truncated hexagonal prism — three pipes

Three equal pipes of regular hexagonal section are joined as shown in a pictorial drawing. The sides of the pipes are each 20 mm and the pipes are jointed at right angles.

To find the development of a pattern for part C:

1 Draw a front view and plan of the assembly.
2 Project lines parallel to the base from all corners of part C in the front view.
3 Mark off along the base six spaces each of distance b — 20 mm — long.
4 At the points so obtained draw verticals to meet the parallel lines from the front view.
5 Complete the development of part C as shown.

Note: The lines along which the developments are bent in order to produce the required three-dimensional article are shown by *thin* lines.

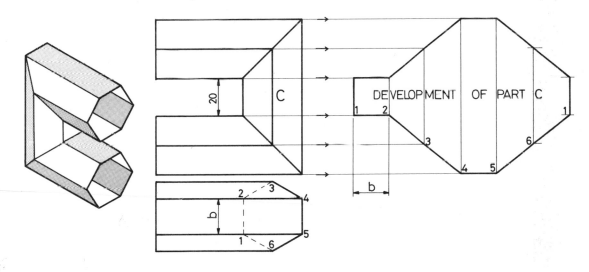

Joints

Development of joint in square pipes

Two pipes of square section of sides 24 mm long are jointed at right angles to each other.

To develop the patterns for both parts of the joint:

1 Draw a front view of the joint.
   Note that this requires a square of side length 24 mm (a) to be drawn as shown.
2 Project lines parallel to the base line of PART A from all corners of PART A in the front view.
3 Project lines parallel to the base line of PART B from all corners of PART B in the front view.
4 Mark off along the base lines of both developments the lengths a of the four sides.
5 At these points on the base line draw lines at right angles to meet the two sets of parallels taken from the front view.
6 Complete the developments of PART A and PART B as shown.

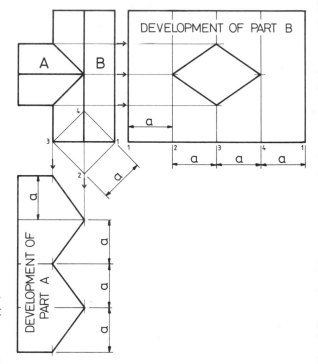

Development of joint in hexagonal pipes

Two pipes of equal section — regular hexagons of 18 mm side lengths — are jointed at 60° to each other.

To develop patterns for both parts of the joint.

1 Draw the front view and plan of the joint.

PART C
2 Draw lines parallel to the base from all corners of PART C in the front view.
3 Mark off along the base line six equal spaces, each 18 mm apart. This gives points 1 to 6 to 1.
4 At the points 1 to 6 to 1 draw verticals to meet the parallels from the front view.
5 Complete the development of PART C as shown.

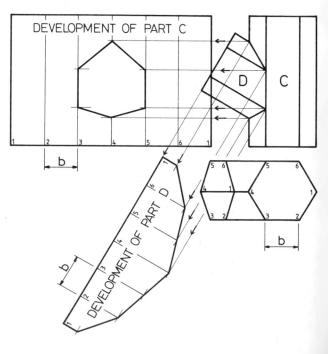

PART D

6 From each corner where D meets C draw parallel lines at right angles to the sides of PART D.

7 Mark off six equal spaces, each 18 mm apart to give points 1 to 6 to 1.

8 Draw lines at right angles to the parallel lines from the front view of PART D to meet the parallel lines.

9 Complete the development of PART D as shown.

Note that bend lines on the developments are shown by thin lines.

Development of joint of hexagonal prisms

A tube of regular hexagonal section with 12 mm sides is jointed at right angles to a regular hexagonal tube of 18 mm sides.

To develop the patterns for both parts of the joint.

1 Draw the front view and plan of the joint.

PART A

2 Draw lines parallel to the base from all corners of PART A shown in the front view.

3 Mark off along the base line six equal lengths, each 18 mm long (length a) to give points 1 to 6 to 1.

4 At points 1 to 6 to 1 draw verticals to meet the parallels from the front view.

5 Complete the development as shown.

PART B

6 Project parallel lines downwards from the plan (or from the front view) of all corners of PART B.

7 Mark off along the vertical base line of the required development six equal spaces of 12 mm (length b).

8 Draw lines at right angles to the base line.

9 Mark off the lengths c at appropriate points.

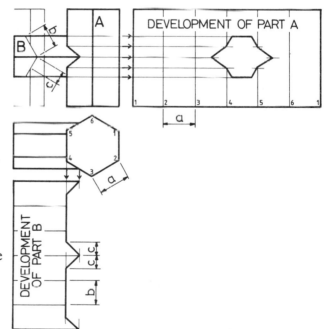

10 Complete the development of PART B as shown.

Note: The front view of PART B includes a half hexagon to obtain the edges of the smaller tube in front view. The lengths b and c are obtained from this half hexagon.

Development of joint between hexagonal pipes

Two hexagonal pipes, one of sides 10 mm, the second of sides 16 mm meet as shown.

To develop patterns for both parts of the joint follow the same general procedure as given for the developments described above. Note the following differences.

1 The two pipes meet with front edges in the same plane.
2 The half regular hexagon construction to obtain front view and plan of the smaller pipe is drawn on the plan. This half hexagon may be drawn either on the front view or on the plan at the reader's discretion.

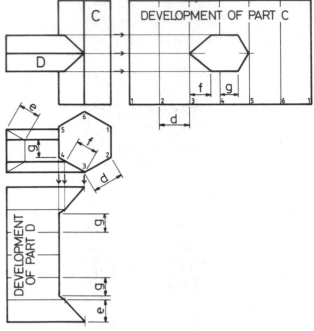

Cylinders

Three pictorial drawings numbered 1, 2 and 3 show the general method of development employed when constructing a pattern for the development of cylindrical parts. It is customary practice to regard a cylinder as a twelve-sided prism when constructing developments of the sides of a cylinder. If very precise patterns are required, a second method of constructing developments for cylinders is also described.

Development of cylinder — Method 1

Cylinder diameter is 50 mm, height 60 mm.

To draw a development of the sides of this cylinder.

1 Draw a front view and plan.
2 Divide the circle of the plan into twelve equal parts.

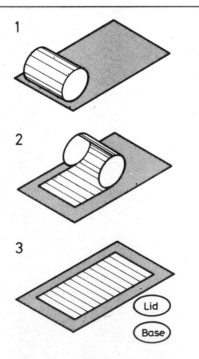

3 Project lines parallel to the base of the front view from top and bottom of the cylinder.

4 Mark off along the base line twelve spaces, each of length a, taken from the plan.

5 Complete the development as shown.

Development of cylinder — Method 2

1 Draw front view and plan of same cylinder as for Method 1.

2 Draw lines parallel to the base from top and bottom of the front view.

3 To find the length of the developed piece use the formula

Circumference of a circle $= \pi D$

In this case $\pi D = 3.14 \times 50 = 157$ mm.

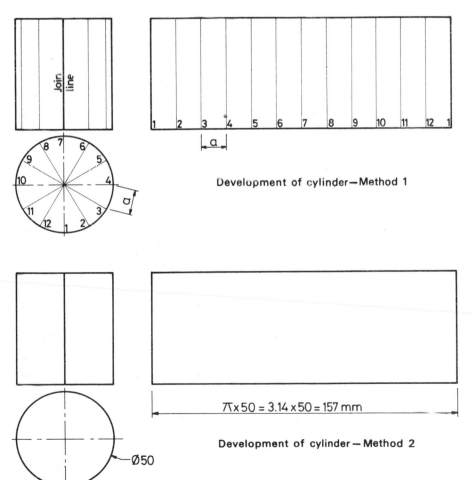

Development of cylinder—Method 1

Development of cylinder — Method 2

$\pi \times 50 = 3.14 \times 50 = 157$ mm

Ø50

Development of truncated cylinder

Three tubes each of diameter 36 mm are jointed at right angles as shown.

To develop a pattern for PART E of this joint:

1 Draw the front view and plan.
2 Divide the circle of PART E in the plan into twelve equal parts.
3 Project from the points 1 to 12 in the plan to the front view.
4 Project a base line for the development.
5 Mark off twelve equally spaced points 1 to 12 to 1 along this base line, the lengths between each taken from the plan. Draw lines at right angles to the base at these points.
6 Where the verticals of points 1 to 12 cross the front view, project lines across the development to meet the verticals 1 to 12 on the development.
7 Draw a fair freehand curve through the points so obtained to complete the development of PART E.

Development of a segment from a bend

A segment from a bend is cylindrical and of diameter 35 mm. Its height increases from 10 mm to 25 mm.

To develop a pattern for segment F:

1 Draw a half plan of the segment and divide the semicircle into six equal parts, representing twelve equal parts of the whole circle.
2 Project points 1 to 7 from the plan to the front view.
3 Draw a base line of length $\pi D = 3.14 \times 35 = 109.9$ mm.
4 Divide this base line into twelve equal parts.
5 Project parallel lines from where the verticals on the front view meet the top and bottom lines of the segment into the development.
6 Complete the development of PART F as shown.

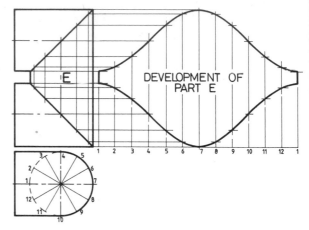

Development of truncated cylinder

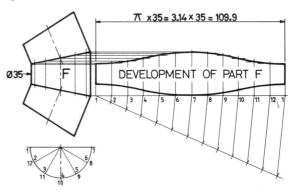

Development of a segment from a bend

Development of a cylindrical chute

A chute of diameter 40 mm and length 70 mm is angled at one end at 60° and curved at the other end to a radius of 40 mm.

To develop the pattern for this chute follow a procedure similar to that for the development of the segment PART F given above.

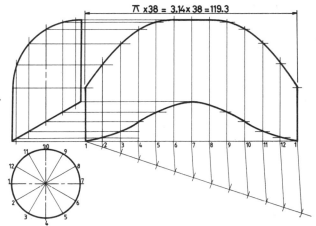

Development of a cylindrical chute

Development of both parts of a joint between cylindrical pipes: 1

Two pipes of diameter 36 mm meet at right angles.

To develop patterns for both parts of the joint:

1. Draw a front view.
2. On the front view draw on the horizontal cylinder a semicircle and divide it into six equal parts.
3. On the front view draw a quadrant of pipe radius and divide it into three equal parts.
4. Draw base lines for both developments. Mark off their lengths — $\pi D = 3.14 \times 36 = 113$ mm.
5. Divide each of these base lines into twelve equal parts and draw lines at right angles to the base line at the points so obtained.
6. Project from the divisions on the semicircle and quadrant in the front view parallel lines across the two developments to obtain points along the curves of the developments.
7. Complete the developments as shown.

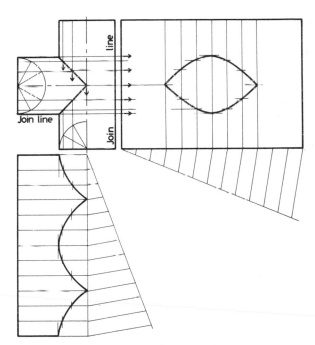

Development of both parts of a joint between cylindrical pipes: 1

Development of both parts of a joint between cylindrical pipes: 2

Two pipes of diameter 32 mm are joined at 45° to each other.

To construct the developments of both parts of the joint:

1 Draw the front view.
2 Proceed as for Example 1 above except that the development of the sloping pipe is taken at right angles to its line of slope.

Note: Compare these two developments. In each example the joint lines of the cylinder have been shown. It is customary to make a joint line along what will be the shortest edge of a development. Thus the development of the branch pipe in Example 1 is a better example of customary practice than is the development of the branch pipe shown in Example 2. Situations may, however, arise when it would be better practice to work a pipe with its joint line as shown in Example 2.

Development of parts of a joint in unequal cylindrical pipes

A right-angled Tee joint between two cylindrical pipes, one of diameter 28 mm, the other of diameter 34 mm, meeting with their fronts in the same plane.

To develop a pattern for the two parts B and C of this joint.

1 Draw the front view and plan of the joint and construct the curve of intersection in the front view.

PART B
2 The development of the pattern for PART B follows the same procedure as for similar developments given on page 83.

PART C
3 The development of PART C follows the same procedure as for the similar

Development of parts of a joint between unequal cylindrical pipes

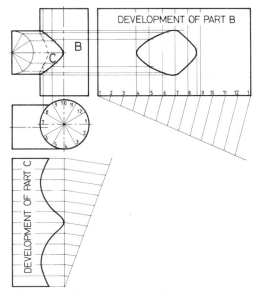

Development of both parts of a joint between cylindrical pipes: 2

development given on page 83. It should be noted that the vertical projections for this development must be taken from where lines from points on the divided semicircle meet the curve of intersection between the two parts. These vertical projection lines are not shown on the given drawing to avoid crowding its construction lines.

Development of part of a two-way connector

This type of connector is sometimes referred to as a *breeches piece*.

The connector splits a cylindrical pipe of 36 mm diameter into two pipes, also of 36 mm diameter. The centre lines of each of the parts of the connector are at 60° to the vertical. Each part is 50 mm along its centre line.

Note that all parts of this system are *right* cylinders.

To construct a development for PART A:
1 Draw the front view. The plan is not really necessary.
2 Draw a circle in projection with the centre line of Part A of diameter 36 mm.
3 Divide the circle into twelve equal parts.
4 Project lines parallel to the centre line of Part A from points 1 to 12 on the circle into the front view.
5 Draw lines at right angles to Part A's centre line at the points where these lines meet the outline of Part A.
6 Mark off twelve equal spaces along the upper of these parallel lines to give lines 1 to 12 to 1.
7 Complete the development of PART A as shown.

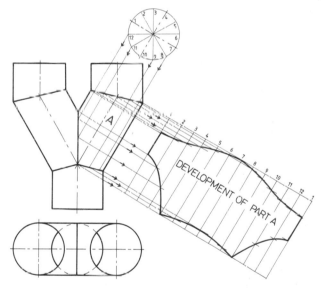

Development of part of a two-way connector

Development of oblique cylinder

The two drawings on this page and page 87 show the differences between development methods for an *oblique* and for a *right* cylinder. Although the two drawings look very similar it should be noted that the base of the drawing on this page is circular and a section taken at right angles to the centre line of the cylinder would produce an ellipse. On the other hand, a section taken at right angles to the centre line of the cylinder shown on page 87 would produce a circle and its base is elliptical.

The oblique cylinder is on a base of 36 mm diameter with its axis at 45° standing overall 40 mm high.

To develop a pattern for the oblique cylinder.

1   Draw a front view and plan.
2   Divide the circle of the plan into twelve equal parts.
3   Project the points 1 to 12 to the base of the front view.
4   Draw lines from these points on the base parallel to the centre line of the front view.
5   Where each of these lines touches the base and the top of the front view project parallel lines at right angles to the centre line across the development.
6   Draw line 1, 1 of the development parallel to the centre line of the front view.
7   Set a compass to the length of any one of the equal spaces on the circle in the plan.
8   Step off these equal spaces from line to line of the development working along the directions shown by the arrows.
9   Complete the development as shown.

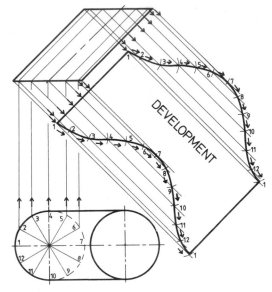

Development of oblique cylinder

Development of right cylinder

A cylinder of diameter 36 mm is cut at top and bottom at 45° as shown.

To construct this development follow the procedures previously shown on page 85.

Note: Examine the two drawings of developments of right and oblique cylinders carefully to ensure an understanding of the differences in constructional methods. The equal spaces taken from the circles of the cylinders have been marked off *along the curve* of the development for the oblique cylinder. They have been marked off along *a parallel line* for the development of the right cylinder.

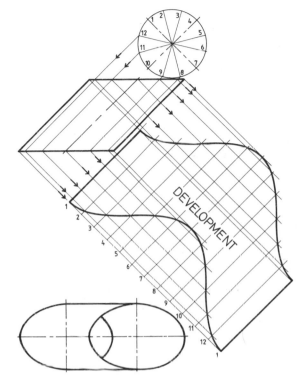

Development of right cylinder

Lobster back bends

The front views of two different types of lobster back segmental bends are shown in the drawings. In the type shown in the drawing marked A, each segment is composed of an equal-size *oblique* cylinder. In the type shown in the drawing marked B, each segment is composed of an equal-size *right* cylinder.

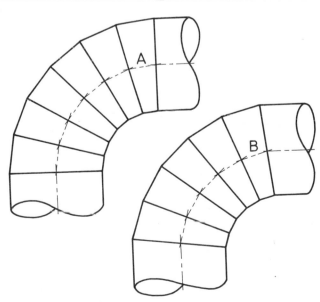

Note: In segment A the circle of the cylinder is along the joint lines. In segment B the circle of the cylinder is along the centre of the segment.

The reader is advised to construct these two developments based on right angled lobster bends jointing pipes of various diameters.

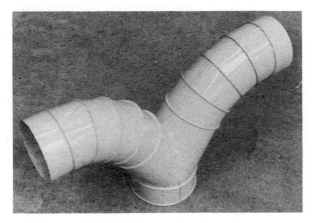

A two-way junction with lobster backs

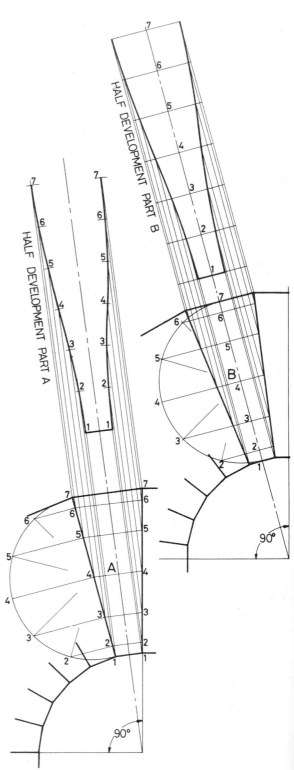

Exercises

The drawings numbered 1 to 17 on this page and on page 90 are front views and plans of tubes and pipes of various shapes and sizes. To obtain dimensions for each of the given drawings count the number of square sides and multiply by 20. Thus the truncated rectangular prism shown by the front view and plan in drawing 1 is 4 × 20 = 80 mm by 2 × 20 = 40 mm by 7 × 20 = 140 mm, with the truncated surface cut at an angle of 45°.

1–17   Construct the development of the shapes shown by the given front views and plans. In the examples with two parts marked A and B develop each of the parts.

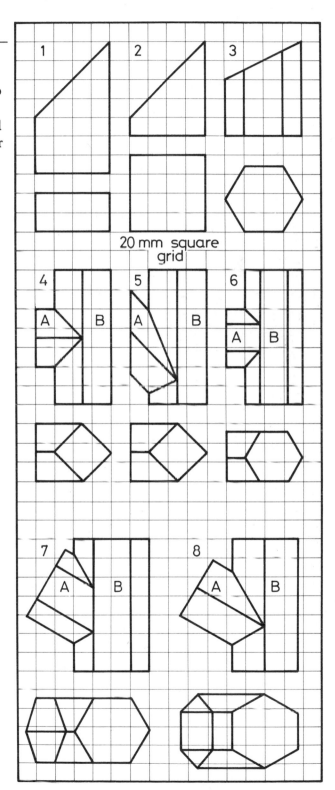

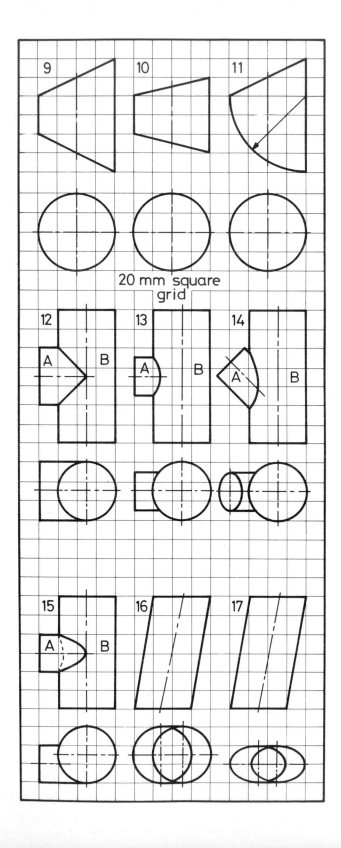

20 mm square grid

18   Construct a development for the part marked A of the connector shown by a front view and plan. Work to a scale of 1:5.

18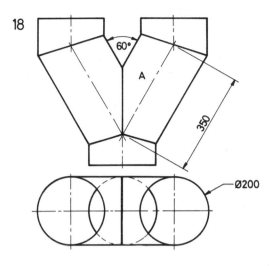

19   Construct a development for any *one* of the segments of the lobster back bend shown in the given front view. Work to a scale of 1:10.

19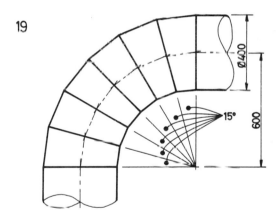

20   Construct a development for any *one* of the segments of the lobster back bend shown in the given drawing. Work to a scale of 1:10.

20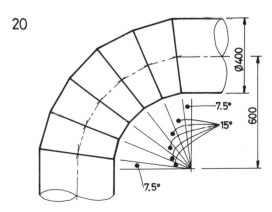

Readers are advised to copy the given drawings to a scale of 1:1 (full size) unless another scale is advised, before attempting to construct answers to the following exercises.

21   Complete the development of the pattern for the branch pipe X shown. (*City and Guilds*)

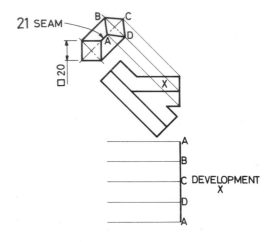

22   The drawing shows a right prism cut by an angular plane. Complete the development of the half pattern. (*City and Guilds*)

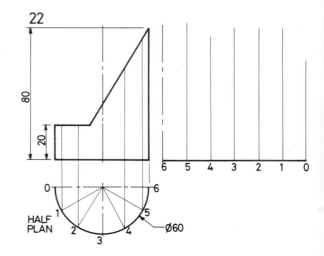

23   The drawing shows a fabricated multiway piece consisting of two cones and a cylinder constructed on the principle of the common central sphere.
(a) Draw, to a scale of 1:10 the layout shown;
(b) Construct the joint line between the cylinder and branches;
(c) Develop the pattern for the cylinder marked A. (*City and Guilds*)

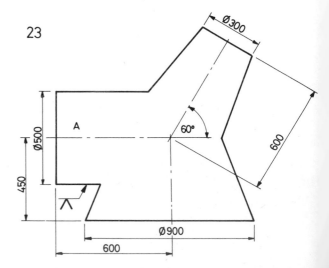

24 Complete a FÚLL PATTERN for the OBLIQUE cylindrical connecting piece shown. (*City and Guilds*)

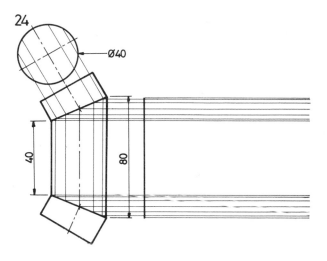

25 From the elevation of the segmental bend shown in the drawing complete a full pattern for the middle segment with the seam in the position indicated. (*City and Guilds*)

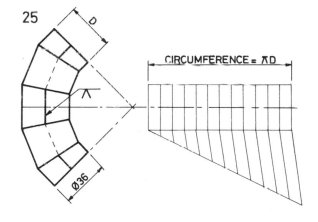

26 The drawing shows a right cylindrical segmental bend fitted with a cylindrical branch pipe. Using a scale of 1:5:
(a) Construct the segmental bend;
(b) Determine the line of intersection between the bend and the branch pipe;
(c) Develop a half pattern for the segment marked A showing the shape of the hole to be cut in it. (*City and Guilds*)

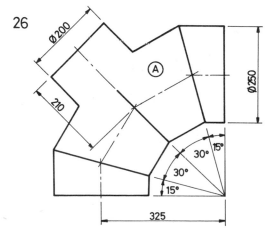

27   The drawing shows a tray with radiused corners. Develop the pattern for the side marked A. (*City and Guilds*)

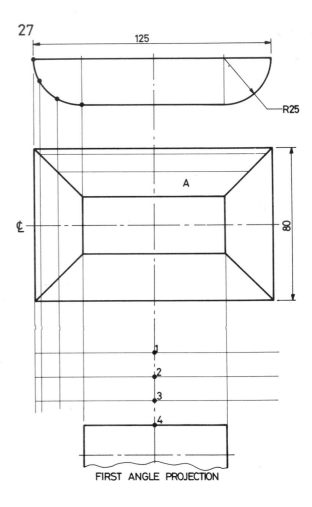

FIRST ANGLE PROJECTION

28   The drawing shows the front and end elevations of an oblique angled square branch pipe fitted to a circular main pipe. Draw the given views to a scale of 1:5 and from them develop:
(a) A full pattern for the square branch pipe;
(b) The true shape of the hole to be cut in the main pipe before rolling to shape.
(*City and Guilds*)

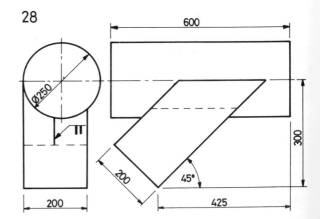

7 Templates for joint lines

When making up moulded sheet metal parts such as channels, troughs, valances or sills meeting at corners to form mitred joints, it may be necessary to construct templates for the shapes of the joint lines. These templates can then be used for marking out on the flat sheets before they are formed to their moulded shapes.

Note: The alternative spelling *templet* will occasionally be seen.

Examples of constructions for templates
Four examples of the methods used for drawing the outlines of templates are given. Note that the methods of parallel line development constructions apply to the constructions for drawing template curves.

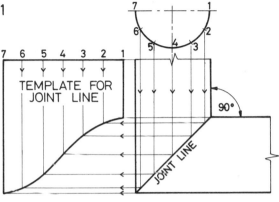

Example 1

Example 1

A right angle joint in a semicircular channel of radius 20 mm.

To construct a template for the mitred corner.

1 Draw the front view and plan of the channel.
2 Divide the semicircle of the front view into six equal parts.
3 Draw base line for the template.
4 Mark off six equal spaces, 1 to 7 along this base line, taking the spacings from the divisions in the front view. Draw lines at right angles at the points 1 to 7.
5 Project the division points from the front view on to the 45° mitre line of the plan.
6 Now project these points on the 45° line at right angles to meet the verticals of the template.
7 Complete the template curves as shown.

Example 2

A coving of radius 28 mm with flats each 6 mm wide.

To construct a template for the mitred corner.

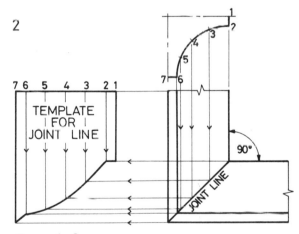

Example 2

1 Draw a front view and plan.
2 Divide the quadrant of the front view into four equal parts.
3 Draw a base line for the template.
4 Mark off the space 1–2 of 6 mm, then four spaces taken from the quadrant of the front view, finishing with another 6 mm space 6–7.
5 Now proceed as for the channel in Example 1 to complete the template curve.

Example 3

A right angle joint in a moulding. Each arc of
the moulding is of radius 10 mm. Each flat is
5 mm wide.

To construct a template for the mitred corner.

1   Draw a front view and plan.
2   Divide each arc of the moulding in the front
    view by taking 30° angles from each radius
    centre.
3   Draw a base line for the template.
4   Mark off space 1–2 of 5 mm width followed
    by twelve equal spaces taken from the
    spacing on the divided front view, finally
    marking space 14–15 again 5 mm wide.
5   Now proceed as explained for the channel of
    Example 1 to complete the template curve.

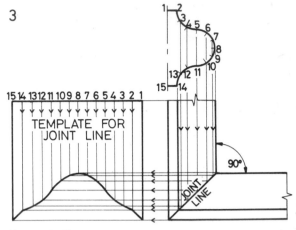

Example 3

Example 4

A right angle joint in a moulding of the outline
shown.

To construct a template for the mitred corner.

1   Draw a front view and a plan.
2   Mark the point 5 on the front view where
    the straight line tangent touches the R22
    arc.
3   Points 6, 7, 8 and 9 on the R22 arc are
    obtained with the aid of a 30°, 60° set
    square.
4   Draw a base line for the template.
5   Mark off spaces 1–2, 2–3 and 3–4, each
    6 mm wide. Mark off space 4–5 taken from
    4–5 on the front view. Mark off space 5–6
    taken from the front view, followed by
    spaces to give points 7, 8, 9 and 10. Finally
    three 6 mm spaces give points 11, 12 and
    13.
6   Now proceed as explained in Example 1 to
    complete the required template.

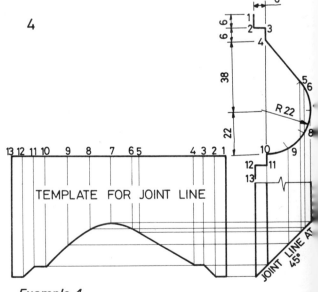

Example 4

Exercises

The drawings numbered 1 to 8 on this page show sections through a variety of channels, mouldings and covings. Construct a corner mitre template for each of the sections given.

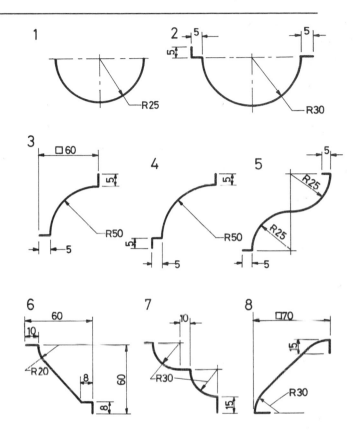

8 True length of lines

The pictorial drawing shows a line placed in the angle between a horizontal plane (HP) and a vertical plane (VP). The line is placed to rest on the HP and is at an angle other than 90° to both the HP and the VP. The front view of the line has been drawn on the VP as viewed in the direction of the arrow F. Its plan has been drawn on the HP as viewed from the direction of the arrow P.

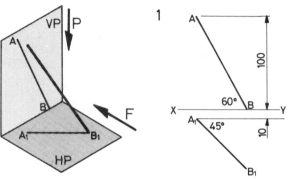

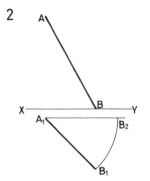

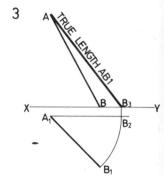

Stages in constructing the true length of a line

Constructing the true length of a line from two given views
Drawing 1

This shows the front view and plan of the line given in the drawing.

Note: Neither view gives the true length of the line AB.

Drawing 2

Commence the construction for finding the true length of the line by drawing in the plan an arc of radius A_1B_1 with the compass centered at A_1. Draw a line parallel to line XY through A_1 to meet the arc at B_2.

Drawing 3

Now project from B_2 to B_3 on line XY. Join AB_3 which gives the true length of the line AB.

Note: Three further examples of the same construction are given. Each shows a front view and plan of a line in a different position relative to the HP and VP. Compare each of the three examples and note that the construction is the same in each case.

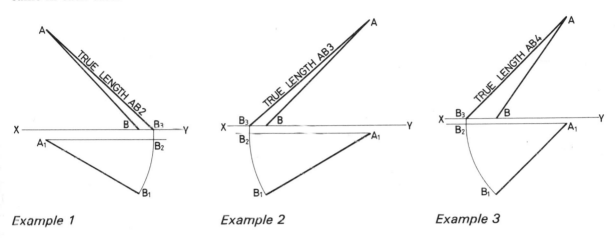

Example 1   *Example 2*   *Example 3*

Exercises

1 Find the true length of line AB.

2 A front view and plan of a line CD are given. Find the true length CD.

3 Find, by construction, the true length of EF.

4 Given the two views of the line GH, find its true length.

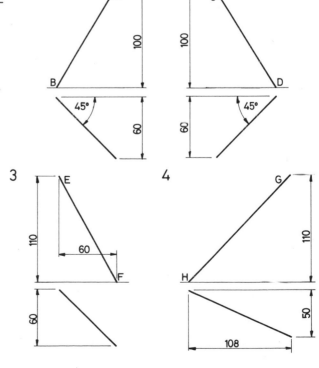

5 Construct the true length of line JK.

6 A support composed of four rods is shown
in front view and plan. Find the true length
of one of the rods LM.

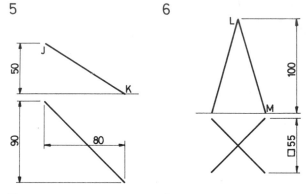

7 A support made from four equal length rods
meeting at N is shown in front view and
plan. Find by construction the true length of
one of the rods NO.

8 Find, by construction, the true length PQ.

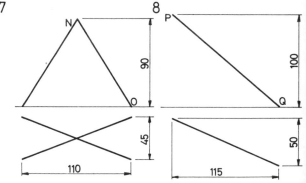

True length of lines — another method
Drawing 1

Given the front view AB and plan A_1B_1, to find
the true length of the line.

1 Draw line $X_1'Y_1$ parallel to AB.
2 At A and at B draw lines at right angles to
AB to cross X_1Y_1.
3 Measure, with a compass, the distance of A_1
below XY.
4 Mark this distance along the line from A
below X_1Y_1 to give A_2.
5 Measure, with a compass, the distance of B_1
below XY.
6 Mark off this distance along the line from B
below X_1Y_1 to give B_2.
7 Join A_2B_2.
8 A_2B_2 is the true length of the line.

Note: The view on X_1Y_1 to give A_2B_2 is called
an *auxiliary view* of the line AB.

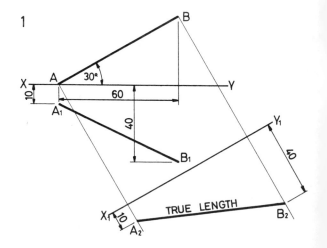

Drawing 2

The true length of a line can also be constructed by projecting an auxiliary view from a plan.

The same dimensions as for drawing 1.

1 Draw X_1Y_1 parallel to C_1D_1.
2 At C_1 and at D_1 draw lines at right angles to C_1D_1 to cross X_1Y_1.
3 As C rests on XY, C_2 must also rest on X_1Y_1.
4 Measure, with a compass, the distance of D above XY.
5 Mark off this distance along the line from D_1 above X_1Y_1 to give D_2.
6 Join C_2D_2.
7 C_2D_2 is the true length of the line CD.

Note: By making use of the same procedure as shown in drawings 1 and 2, projections can be made in the opposite directions to those shown in drawings 1 and 2.

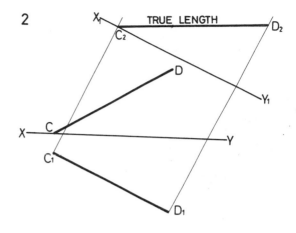

Drawing 3

The true length has been constructed by projecting from the front view *above* the line.

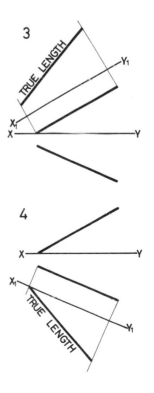

Drawing 4

The true length has been constructed by projecting from the plan *below* the line.

Exercises

The reader is advised to copy the given drawings to a scale of 1:1 (full size) before attempting to draw the required solutions.

1   Three views of a line diagram representing a Scotch derrick are given. Complete:
(a) The view on arrow X to give the true lengths of back legs A–B;
(b) The view on arrow Y to give the true length of jib C–D. (*City and Guilds*)

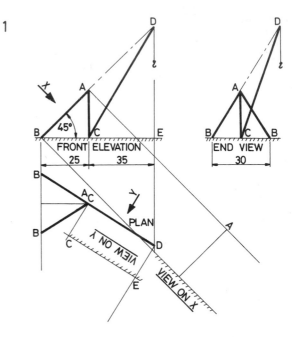

2   A–B in the given drawing represents the centre line of the web of a bracing beam between two offset columns. Determine the true length of the line A–B. (*City and Guilds*)

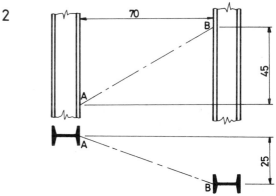

3   Part of a welded portal knee joint is shown. Project a sectional view on B–B to show the true position of the site bolt holes and the true length of 'weld all round' required. (*City and Guilds*)

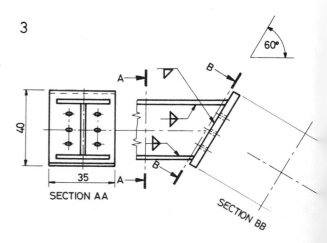

9 Radial line development

Square pyramids

Development of right square pyramid
The pyramid is of a square base of sides 40 mm long and of height 55 mm.

To develop the pattern for the sides of the pyramid:

1 Draw a front view and plan.
2 Find the *true* length of edge AB. With a compass centred at A and set to radius AB, draw arc BC to meet a horizontal line through the apex A of the pyramid. Project from C on to the ground line of the front view. The line b is the true length of edge AB. This follows the construction shown on page 98.
3 Draw an arc of radius b.
4 Set a compass to a — the side length of the square base.
5 Mark off along the arc of radius b four arcs of radius a.
6 Complete the required development as shown.

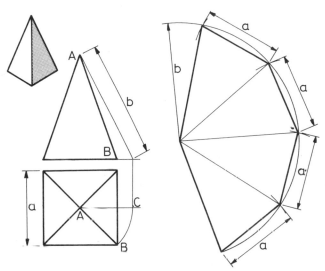

Development of right square pyramid

Development of frustum of right square pyramid
The pyramid is of a square base of sides 34 mm and height 55 mm cut horizontally 18 mm above the base.

To develop a pattern for the sides of the frustum:

1 Draw front view and plan.
2 Find the true length of the edge CD to give length d.
3 Project top line EF on to line d to give true length e.
4 Draw an arc of radius d and step off four base side lengths c along the arc.
5 From the same centre as for arc d draw an arc of radius e.
6 Complete the development as shown.

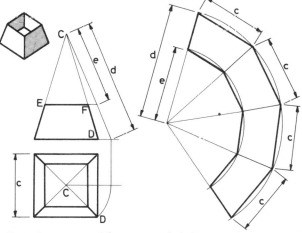

Development of frustum of right square pyramid

Development of truncated right square pyramid

The base is of 34 mm sides, height 60 mm truncated at 30° to horizontal. Line 2–3 is 8 mm above base.

To develop a pattern for the sides of the truncated pyramid:

1. Draw front view and plan.
2. Find true length of one edge to give length f.
3. From edges 2–3 and 1–4 in the front view project on to line f to give the two true lengths g and h.
4. Draw an arc of radius f and step off four base side lengths along the arc.
5. From the same centre as for arc f draw arcs of radius g and h to give points 1, 2, 3, 4 and 1 on the development.
6. Complete the development as shown.

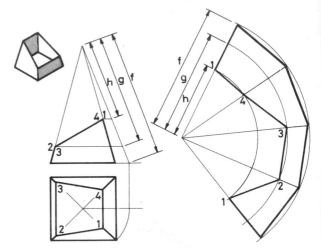

Development of truncated right square pyramid

Rectangular pyramids

Development of frustum of right rectangular pyramid

The pyramid base is 50 mm by 25 mm, height 70 mm, frustum 20 mm high.

To develop a pattern for the sides of the frustum:

1. Draw front view and plan.
2. Construct the true length of an edge of the pyramid.
3. Project the upper line of the front view on to the true length line.
4. Complete the development as shown.

Note: The methods involved in this example are similar to those shown for the development of the frustum of a square pyramid given on page 103. The side lengths AB, BC, CD and DA of the rectangular base are marked off around the arc of true length radius on the development.

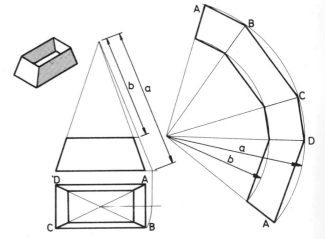

Development of frustum of right rectangular pyramid

Development of truncated right rectangular pyramid

The pyramid is of base 50 mm by 30 mm and height 50 mm. Truncation commences 10 mm vertically from base to finish 20 mm vertically from base.

To develop a pattern for the sides of the truncated pyramid:

1   Draw front view and plan.
2   Construct the true length of an edge to give length a.
3   Project from the top and bottom of the truncation line on to line a to give lengths b and c.
4   Draw an arc of radius a. Step off along this arc the side lengths of the rectangle to give points 1, 2, 3, 4 and 1.
5   From the centre of arc a draw two other arcs of radius b and c.
6   Complete the development as shown.

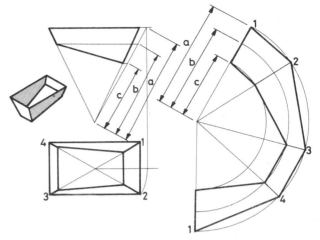

Development of truncated right rectangular pyramid

A hood formed from a square pyramid

Hexagonal pyramids

Right hexagonal pyramids

If the hexagon in plan is as shown in the upper and lower examples on page 106 it is necessary to find, by construction, the true length of one of the complete edges of the pyramid. If the hexagon in plan is as shown in the middle example the front view already shows the true length of one of the complete pyramid edges, and a true length construction is then unnecessary.

Development of truncated right hexagonal pyramid

First example

The base sides are 20 mm, height is 50 mm, truncated 45°, 12 mm from base.

1 Draw front view and plan. Note the part end view construction to obtain the width a.
2 Construct A1 — the true length of an edge.
3 Project points B, C and D on to the true length line.
4 Draw arcs of radii A1, AB_1, AC_1 and AD_1.
5 Mark off points 1 to 6 to 1 along the arc A1. Lengths same as hexagon base side.
6 Complete the development as shown.

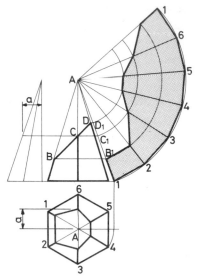

Development of truncated right hexagonal pyramid. First example

Second example

The same hexagonal pyramid but truncated at 30° as shown.

1 Draw outline half plan and front view as in drawing 1.
2 True length is given by line EF.
3 Project points G, H and J on to EF.
4 Complete the development as shown in drawing 2.

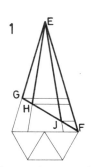

Second example

Third example

The hexagon sides are 20 mm, height is 55 mm, upper edges are 25 mm above base, lower truncation at 30°.

1 Draw front view and plan.
2 Construct true lengths a, b, c and d.
3 With these true lengths as radii construct the development as shown.

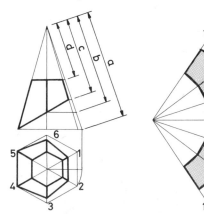

Third example

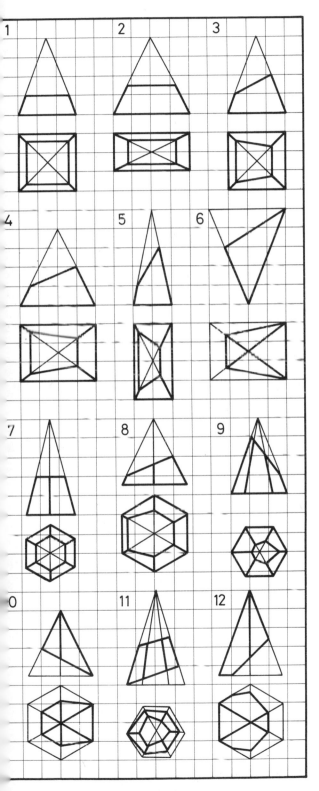

Exercises

The fifteen drawings are front views and plans of a variety of forms, the developments of which are required. To obtain the dimensions of each, count the number of sides of the 20 mm squares of the grid along each part of the two views.

Develop the patterns required for making the forms in sheet metal of each of the fifteen examples.

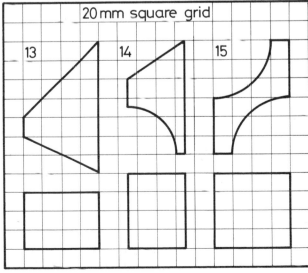

20 mm square grid

The three photographs on this page are examples of sheet metal forms, the patterns for which were developed by radial line methods.

A funnel cone — an example of a frustum of a cone

A transition piece in the form of a frustum of a cone

A ventilation cowling

Right cones

The development of the surfaces of right cones

When developing patterns for right cones it is imagined that the cone is placed on a flat surface and rolled around its apex. This is shown in a pictorial drawing.

Two methods may be used for the developments of right cones. The first method is that

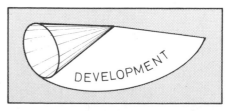

most commonly employed when developing patterns for sheet metal working.

Development of right cone — Method 1

The cone is of base diameter 56 mm and height 80 mm.

1 Draw front view and plan of cone.
2 Divide the circle of the plan into twelve equal parts.
3 Join the points 1–12 on the circle to its centre.
4 Project points 1–12 to the base of the front view.
5 Join these points to A, the apex of the cone.
6 A7 (or A1) is the true length of any one of the lines from A to the equally spaced points on the base.
7 Draw an arc of radius L.
8 Step off, with a compass, twelve spaces along the arc, each of length a, taken from a in the plan.
9 Complete the development as shown.

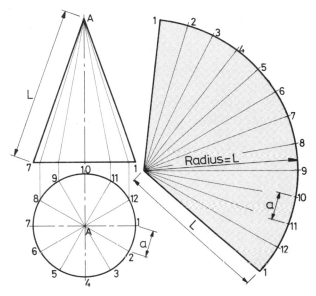

Development of right cone — Method 1

Development of right cone — Method 2

The cone is of diameter 54 mm and height 75 mm.

1 Draw front view and plan.
2 Measure the length L. In this example L = 79 mm.
3 Calculate the angle for the sector of radius L which forms the development. Use the formula:

$$\text{angle of sector} = \frac{360 \times R^\circ}{L}$$

In this example,

$$\text{angle of sector} = \frac{360 \times 27}{79} = 123^\circ$$

4 Draw an arc of radius L.
5 With a protractor mark off an angle of 123° within this arc to complete the development.

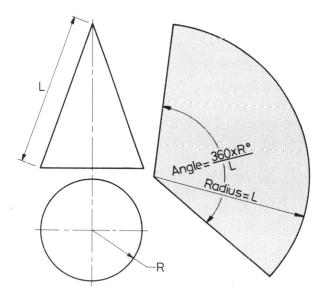

Development of right cone — Method 2

Development of truncated right cone

Drawings 1, 2 and 3 show the stages of construction necessary for making a development of a truncated right cone. The third, and final stage, is shown in a drawing of enlarged scale.

The cone is of base diameter 60 mm and height 80 mm truncated at 45° to its central axis, with the lowest point of the truncation 15 mm vertically above the base.

Stage 1

1 Draw front view and plan of the cone.
2 Divide its base circle in the plan into twelve equal parts giving points 1 to 12.
3 Join points 1 to 12 to the centre of the circle.
4 Project the twelve points into the base of the front view.
5 Join these points to the apex A of the front view.
6 Draw an arc of radius A1.
7 Step off twelve equal spaces taken from the plan along the arc to give points 1 to 12 to 1.
8 Draw straight lines from each of the points 1 to 12 to A.

Stage 2

At points 1 to 7 in the front view draw lines parallel to the base to meet line AB.

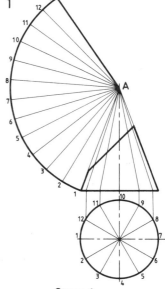

1

Stage 1

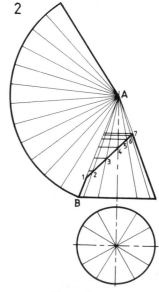

2

Stage 2

Stage 3

1 With a compass centred at A and set to AC draw an arc to meet lines A2 and A12.
2 With the compass centred at A and set to AD draw an arc to meet lines A3 and A11.
3 Continue in this manner with compasses set in turn to AE, AF, AG and AH, to obtain points 4 to 10 on the curve of the development.
4 Finally set the compass to radius A1 and draw an arc on the left-hand line A1.
5 Draw a fair freehand curve through the points so constructed to complete the development.

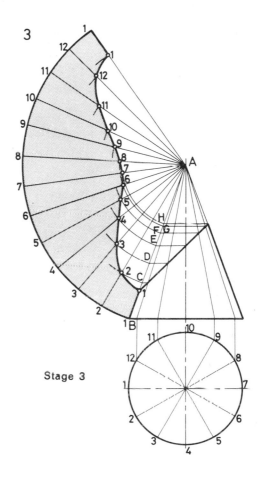

Stage 3

Right cones

Examples of developments numbered 1, 2 and 3 of parts of right cones are given on this page and page 112. The procedures employed are the same as those given on pages 109 and 110.

Drawing 1

The frustum of a cone is of the dimensions given with the frustum standing 18 mm high.

This example uses Method 2 explained on page 109.

Note: Both arcs of the development are centred at the apex A.

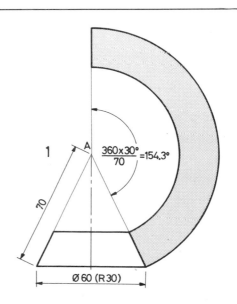

$$\frac{360 \times 30°}{70} = 154.3°$$

Ø 60 (R 30)

Drawing 2

The cone base diameter is 90 mm and height 105 mm. Lower truncation is as shown at 30°. Upper truncation is also at 30° with highest point 80 mm above the base.

The methods of constructing the development are the same as those described on page 110.

Note: Only half of the plan is required. This is shown in construction lines only. The half plan in construction is quite sufficient to give the required twelve divisions of the base to be transferred to the development arc.

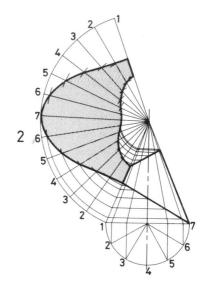

Drawing 3

The cone diameter is 100 mm, height 120 mm, height of frustum 100 mm. The curved surface of radius 100 mm is centred at point 1 on the base.

The method of construction of the development again follows the procedure described on page 110.

Note: The upper arc of the development is drawn with a compass centred at A.

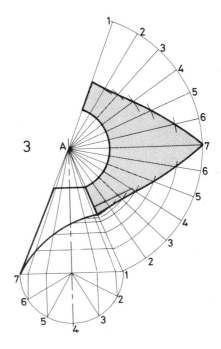

Exercises

The dimensioned drawings numbered 1 to 12 are front views of cones or parts of right cones. Construct developments for each of the shapes shown.

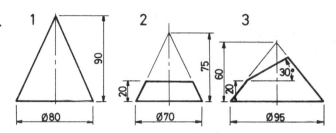

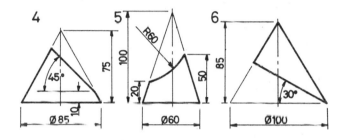

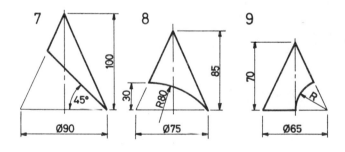

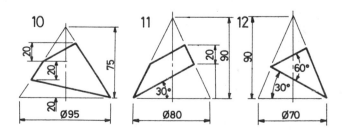

13 Copy the given drawing scale 1:1 and construct a development for the part A.

14 Copy the given drawing scale 1:1. Construct the development pattern for part B.

15 Copy the given drawing. Each cylindrical pipe joint to the connecting piece is based on a common central sphere. The connecting piece is part of a right cone. Develop a pattern for the connecting piece part C.

16 The connecting piece D is part of a right cone. The joints between part D and the two cylindrical pipes are based on the principle of the common central sphere. Construct a pattern for the connector part D.

The three photographs on this page and page 115 show sheet metal constructions, parts of which involve the drawing of patterns for the development of oblique cones. See also pages 115 and 117.

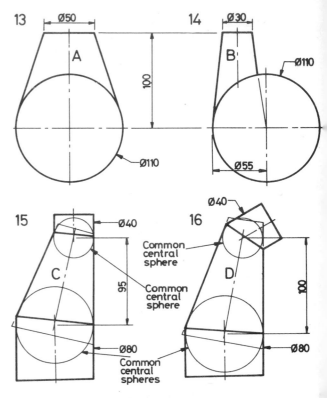

An example of a cone and sphere intersection

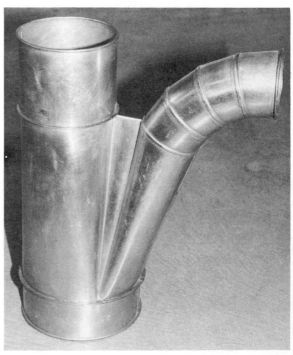

A junction piece

Oblique cones

The methods of constructing the development
for an oblique cone are shown in three stages on
this page and page 116. The third drawing has
been made to an enlarged scale.

Note: Compare the procedure for constructing
the development of an oblique cone given on
this page with that for a right cone given on
page 109. Two major differences will be noted.

1 In the first stage arcs are taken from the
   twelve equal divisions on the base circle in
   the plane, with the arc centred at the apex
   A.
2 The twelve equal spaces taken from the
   twelve divisions of the base circle are
   marked off *along the curve* of the
   development of an oblique cone and *along
   the arc* of the true length radius of the right
   cone.

The oblique cone is of base diameter 55 mm
and vertical height 80 mm with its axis at 60°
to the base.

*A junction between two pipes and an oblique
cone*

Stage 1

1 Draw front view and plan.
2 Divide the circle of the base in the plan into
   twelve equal parts.
3 Taking points 2 to 6 in turn and with a
   compass centred at the apex A draw arcs of
   radius A2, A3, A4, A5 and A6 to meet the
   centre line.
4 Project these points on the centre line on to
   the base of the front view.
5 Join the points 1 to 7 on the front view base
   to A.

Stage 2

With a compass centred at A and with radii of
A1, A2 to A7 in turn draw a series of arcs.

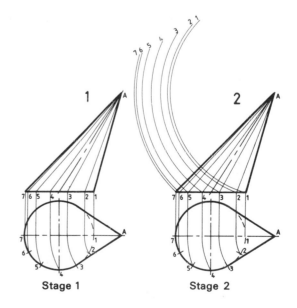

Stage 1   Stage 2

Stage 3

1 Set a compass to one of the twelve equal
   spaces on the plan circle.
2 Commencing at point 1 on line A7 step off
   this space on to the next arc from A to give
   point 2 on the development.
3 With the compass at point 2 step off the
   space on to the next arc from A to give point
   3 on the development.
4 Continue in this way to complete the points
   1 to 7 to 1 on the development.
5 Join the points so obtained with a fair
   freehand curve to complete the required
   development.

Examples of developments of oblique cones

Example 1

The oblique cone is of base diameter 52 mm,
vertical height 80 mm with axis at 65° to base.
The height of frustum is 26 mm.

To develop a pattern for the frustum

1 Draw the front view.
2 Draw a half plan in construction lines.
3 Divide the half plan into six equal parts.
4 In the plan with a compass centred at A
   draw arcs of radii A2, A3, A4, A5 and A6
   to meet the base of the front view.
5 Join the points so obtained to the apex A.
   These lines cross the upper edge of the
   frustum.
6 From the points on the base of the front
   view and the upper edge of the frustum
   draw arcs centred at A.
7 With a compass set to one of the divisions
   in the plan, mark off the twelve divisions
   along the arcs taken from the base line of
   the front view.
8 Join these points 1 to 7 to 1 to A.
9 With a compass centred at A draw arcs
   from the points on the upper edge of the

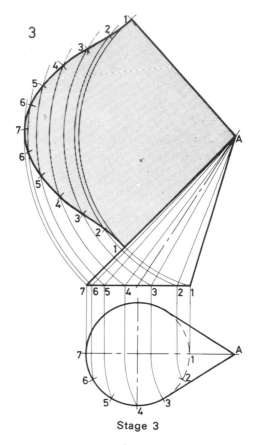

Stage 3

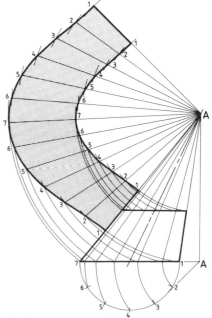

Example 1

frustum to cross the lines A1 to A7 to A1
on the development.
10   Complete the development as shown.

Example 2

The cone base diameter is 76 mm, vertical
height 130 mm, axis at 66°, upper edge 30 mm
from apex, lower edge 20° to base.

To develop a pattern for this part of an oblique
cone:

1   Follow the same procedure as for Example 1
up to stage 8. Also to obtain the curve of the
development nearest V, the same procedure
is followed as for finding the upper curve of
the development in Example 1.
Note: The lower curve includes the extra
stages 2 to 5.
2   Project verticals to the base of the front view
from points 2, 3, 4, 5 and 6 in the plan.
3   Join the points on the base to the apex V by
straight lines.
4   Where these lines meet the truncation line
of the front view draw lines parallel to the
base to give points B, C, D, E and F.
5   With a compass centred at V draw arcs
through A, B to F to meet lines V1, V2 to
V7 to V1 to give A, B to A on the
development.
6   Complete the required development as
shown.

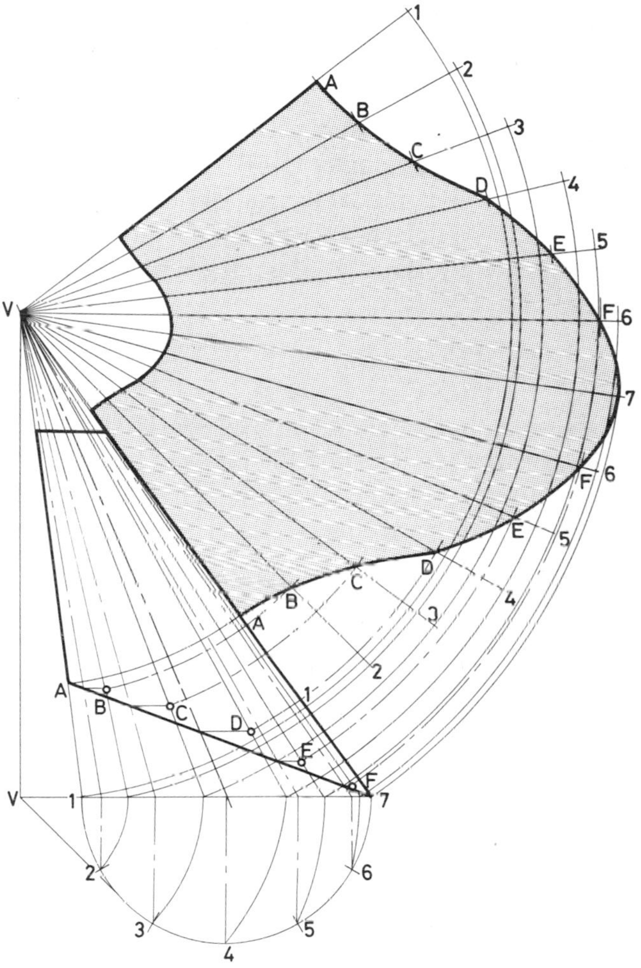

Example 2

Worked examples
Three examples of solutions of radial line
development methods to sheet metal articles
which include parts of right cones are shown on
page 118.

The reader is advised to attempt working these
solutions following the descriptions of
constructions given in the previous pages. Some
notes are given for each of the three solutions
shown.

Example and solution 1

A tube of diameter 30 mm is jointed to a right conical spout, the apex of which is 60 mm from the centre of the cylindrical tube. The cone meets the tube tangentially. Develop a pattern for the conical spout.

Note: The two construction lines A_1B and A_1C are drawn at right angles to AB and AC to determine the points of tangency of the cone to the cylinder. The construction to obtain the development follows the procedure given on page 111.

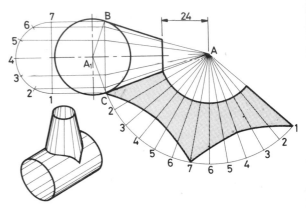

Example and solution 1

Example and solution 2

A shade is composed of two frustums of half cones each of base radius 100 mm and height 250 mm, and standing 125 mm high. The two half cones are joined by rectangular pieces of length 125 mm. Develop a scale 1:5 half pattern for the shade.

Note: In the half development the part $A_1B_1F_1D_1$ is a rectangle. Otherwise the procedure for developing the half cone parts of the shade follows the construction described on page 111.

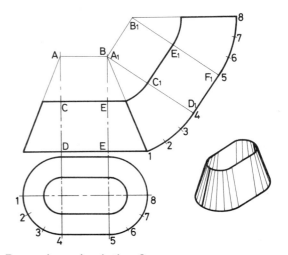

Example and solution 2

Example and solution 3

A shield is made up of a half cone of base radius 100 mm and height 325 mm and standing 180 mm high and side pieces 125 mm wide at the base and 60 mm wide at the top. Develop a scale 1:5 pattern for the shield.

Note: The development again follows the construction described on page 111.

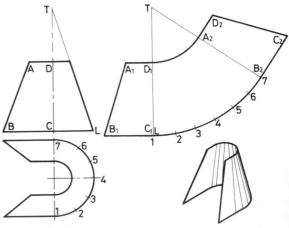

Example and solution 3

Tapered lobster back

A front view of a tapered lobster back bend made up of a series of part right cones jointed on the basis of common central spheres is shown. Half developments of segments A and E of the bend are also given.

The constructions for these two segments follow closely the methods described on pages 111 and 112.

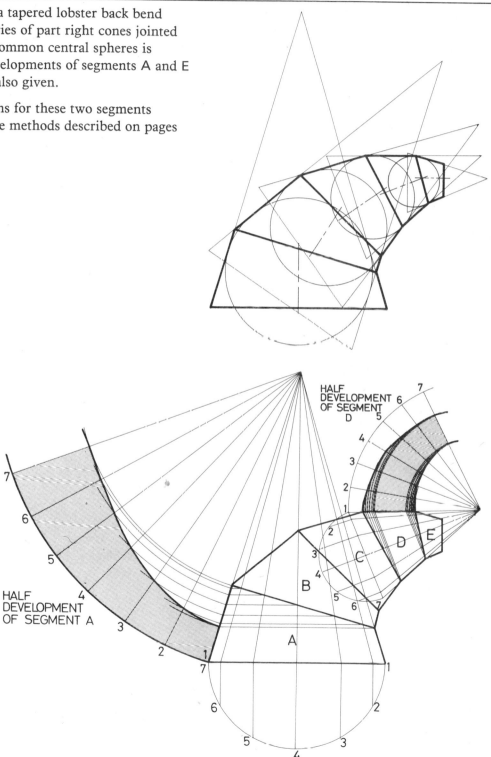

HALF DEVELOPMENT OF SEGMENT D

HALF DEVELOPMENT OF SEGMENT A

Exercises

The drawings numbered 1 to 8 are all front views and plans of oblique cones or parts of oblique cones. Taking each example in turn and working to the dimensions assessed from the sides of the 20 mm squares of the grid, construct scale 1:1 developments for each of the eight shapes.

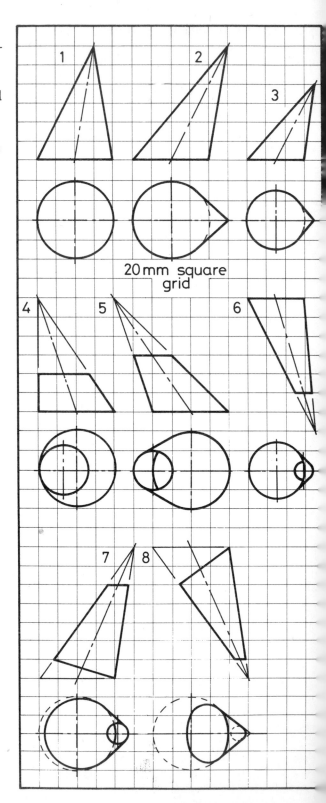

20 mm square grid

9 The drawing shows a part oblique conical outlet jointed to a cylindrical tube. Construct a scale 1:1 development for the part conical outlet.

10 The drawing shows a second example of a part oblique conical outlet jointed to a cylindrical tube. Construct a scale 1:1 development for the outlet.

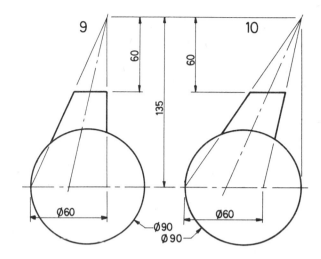

11 Copy, scale 1:10, the given front view and plan of a machine guard to be made from 2 mm thick carbon mild steel. Construct a scale 1:10 half pattern for the guard.

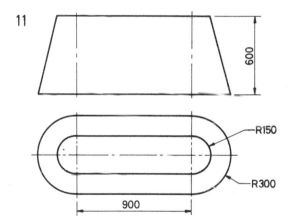

12 A shield is shown in a front view and plan drawing. Develop to scale 1:5 a full pattern for the shield.

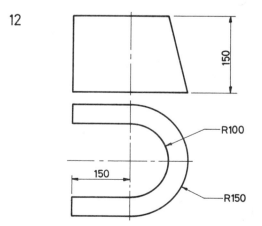

13 Draw the given front view and end view of a cowling. Construct a full size (scale 1:1) development for the cowling.

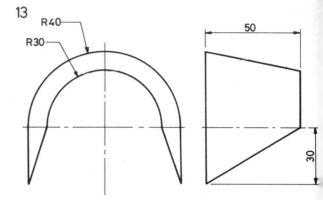

14 A three-view orthographic drawing of a chute is given. Copy the drawing, scale 1:1. Construct a scale 1:1 development for the chute.

The student is advised to copy the given drawings scale 1:1 (unless a different scale is indicated) before attempting the solutions to Exercises 15 to 22.

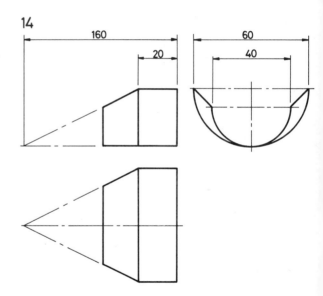

15 The drawing shows an elevation and a half plan of a frustum of a right pyramid. Develop a half pattern placing the joint along line X–X. (*City and Guilds*)

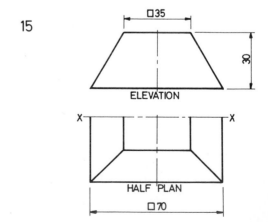

16 The drawing shows a two-point right
conical nozzle connected to a vertical
cylindrical pipe.
(a) Complete the partly drawn joint lines
using the principle of the common central
sphere;
(b) Develop a HALF PATTERN for one
of the nozzles with the seams in the
position indicated. (*City and Guilds*)

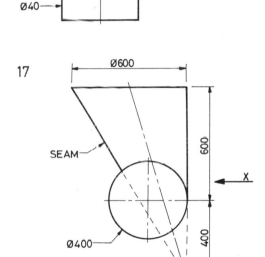

17 The drawing shows a frustum of an
oblique cone fitted to a cylinder. Using a
scale of 1:10:
(a) Develop a half pattern for this cone;
(b) Draw an elevation in the direction of
the arrow X showing a short length of the
cylinder and the line of intersection. (*City
and Guilds*)

18 The drawing shows a connecting piece
between a right cone and two right
cylinders, together with a partly completed
half pattern for the right cone. Complete
the half pattern. (*City and Guilds*)

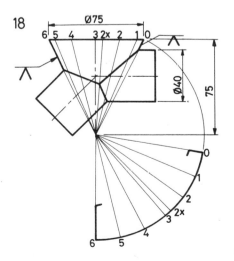

19 The drawing shows a filler spout in the form of a right conic frustum, which is to be attached to a flat side of a tank.
(a) Draw scale 1:1 the given view;
(b) Develop the pattern of the spout;
(c) Project the shape of the hole to be cut in the tank X–X. (*City and Guilds*)

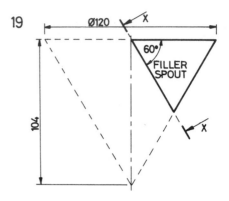

20 Using the method of cutting planes, draw the curve of intersection between the right conical base and the square section pipe given in elevation and half plan and hence develop a suitable template for the conical base. (*City and Guilds*)

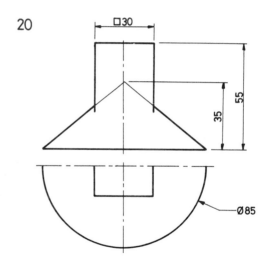

21 The drawing shows views of a breeches piece constructed from cone frustums. To a scale of 1:10
(a) Develop a suitable half pattern for the branch A;
(b) Project the TRUE SHAPE of the joint plane X–X. (*City and Guilds*)

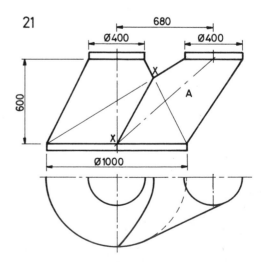

22   The drawing shows a right conical outlet fitted to the base of a hemisphere.
(a) Set out the views given, scale 1:1;
(b) Use cutting planes to plot the line of intersection;
(c) Develop a half pattern for the conical outlet. (*City and Guilds*)

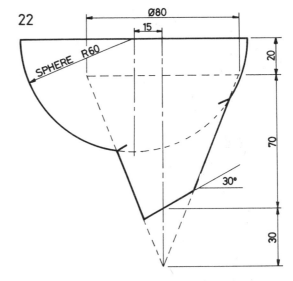

10 Development by triangulation

Development by triangulation is the third of the three main methods of construction for developing the patterns required for forming shapes in sheet metal.

The method is known as development by triangulation because it depends upon the drawing of series of triangles in order to plot points on the outlines of developments.

The method of development by triangulation is important because it can be used for constructing patterns which can also be developed by radial line methods. A close examination of the examples given of radial line developments will show that they also could depend upon triangle constructions.

Note: In all work involving development by triangulation the most important feature is to make certain that the lengths of *all* triangle sides are actual *true lengths*.

Development of an oblique square pyramid

1 Draw the front view and plan.
2 Construct the true lengths VA and VB. Note the *true length diagram* to the right of the front view.
3 Construct the *true shape* of the triangles ABV, BCV, CDV and ADV from the plan and true length diagram. Thus AB, BC, CD and DA of the development are taken from the plan. AV, BV, CV and DV are taken from the *true length diagram*.

Development of a square to rectangular connector

Note: This is *not* a pyramid.

1 Construct true length diagrams on the right of the front view. The heights V_1V and W_1W are projected from the front view. The base lengths of the true length diagrams — V_1D, V_1A, W_1C and W_1B — are taken from the plan.

A square to rectangle transformer

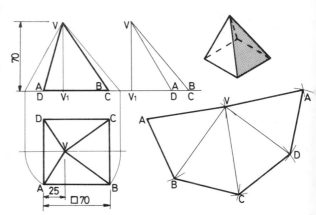

Development of an oblique square pyramid

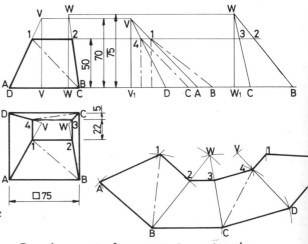

Development of a square to rectangle connector

2 Two other true lengths are required — the diagonal B1 and the diagonal C4.

3 The development can now be constructed from the series of triangles whose edges are the true lengths from the true length diagrams or taken direct from the plan.

Twisted square transformers

Development of twisted square transformer

The base square is of side lengths 70 mm, height 90 mm.

1 Draw front view and plan.

2 In this example the lines A1, B1 in the front view *are* true lengths. The lines AB and 1–2 are also true lengths in the plan. Thus the development can be constructed from true lengths taken directly from the two given views.

3 Construct the adjoining triangles to complete the development.

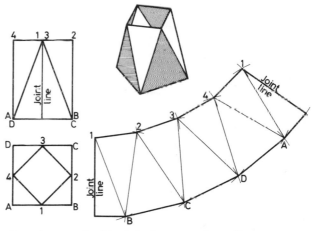

Development of twisted square transformer

Development of twisted square transformer

The base is a square of 70 mm sides, height 80 mm. The top is a square of 36 mm sides.

Two true lengths are required. A true length diagram is drawn to the right of the front view.

1 Draw front view and plan.

2 Construct true length diagram.

3 Construct the adjoining triangles to complete development.

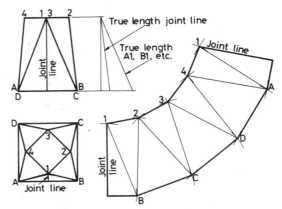

Development of twisted square transformer

Development of twisted rectangular transformer

The rectangles are of sides 70 mm by 25 mm, height 90 mm.

1 Draw front and end views and a plan.
2 Again, in this example, no true length diagram is necessary and in fact the development can be constructed without triangulation.
3 The true shape of the rear of the transformer is given in the front view. Thus the quadrilateral CD34 can be drawn.
4 In the development line 1–4 must be at 90° to line D4 and line 1–4 true length can be taken direct from the plan, as can line AD. Quadrilateral AD14 can be drawn.
5 BC23 is a quadrilateral of the same shape and sizes as CD34. Thus it can be drawn touching along line C3.
6 Finally, quadrilateral AB21 is the same shape as quadrilateral AD14. Thus it also can be drawn to complete the required development.

The sheet metal constructions shown in the three photographs include parts, the patterns for which required development by triangulation methods.

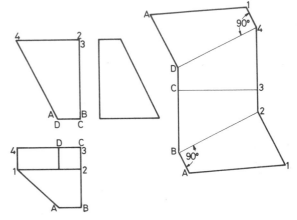

Development of twisted rectangular transformer

A circle to square transformer

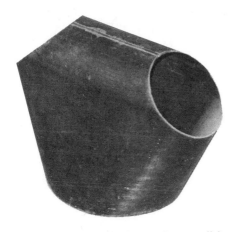

A breeches piece connected to pipes, forming a junction

A breeches piece made from sheet mild steel

Square to circle transformers

Three examples of developments of patterns for square to circle transformers are shown on this page and on page 130. They can be worked from transformers of the following dimensions:

Each square base is of sides 80 mm long. Each circular outlet is of 68 mm diameter. The heights are — Example 1, 50 mm; Example 2, 60 mm; Example 3, 70 mm.

The *true length diagrams* drawn to the right of each of the front views of the three examples

become more complicated because of the different positions of the circular outlet in relation to the square base in the three examples. In Example 1 only three true lengths need to be constructed to draw the development. In Example 2 eight true lengths are required. In Example 3 twelve true length constructions become necessary. In all cases the bases of the triangles forming the true length diagrams are taken directly from the plan view drawings.

Example 1

The following true lengths have to be constructed. The length of the joint line A1; the length B1, which is the same as C1, D1 and E1; the length of B2, which is the same as B3, C1, C2, D1, D2, E1, E2. From these true lengths the side-by-side triangles for the development can be constructed, adjusting a compass to each triangle side length in turn and building up the triangles from crossing arcs drawn with the compass. The lengths 1−2, 2−3 and 3−1 are taken direct from one of the twelve divisions in the plan circle.

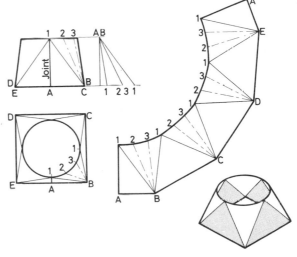

Example 1

Example 2

This example shows a HALF PATTERN only. True lengths need to be constructed for the joint line A1; B1, B2, B3 and B4; C4, C5, C6 and C7. AB, BC and CD are taken direct from the plan and D7 taken direct from the front view height. The lengths 1–2, 2–3 and so on are taken directly from the twelve divisions in the plan circle with the aid of a compass.

Example 3

True lengths need to be constructed for B1, B2, B3 and B4; C4, C5, C6 and C7; D7, D8, D9; E11 and E12 are the same. True lengths AB, BC, CD, DE and DA are taken direct from the plan. E10 = E1 can be taken from the front view, as can D10. The lengths 1–2, 3–4 and so on are taken from the twelve divisions in the plan circle with the aid of a compass.

Square to circle transformers — more examples
Example 1

The square is of sides 90 mm. The circle is of diameter 60 mm, the centre vertically above the mid-point of the square base. Height is 60 mm. Bottom edge slopes at 30° as shown.

Note: There are four true length diagrams as follows:

1   To find true length A1.
2   To find true lengths B1, B2, B3 and B4.
3   To find true lengths C4, C5, C6 and C7.
4   To find true length D7.

Only a half pattern is shown. The transformer is to be made in two parts to be joined to each other along lines A1 and D7.

5   Commence the development by constructing triangle BC4.
6   From B strike arcs B3, B2 and B1.

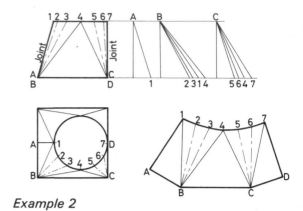

Example 2

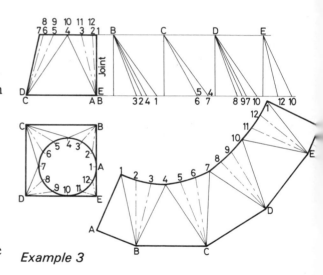

Example 3

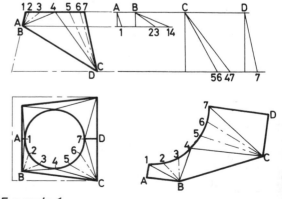

Example 1

7 From 4 strike arcs equal to one of the plan circle divisions to cross arc B3 at 3. From 3 strike the same arc to obtain 2. Then from 3 strike arc to obtain 1. Join 1, 2, 3, 4 with a fair freehand curve.

8 Now construct triangle AB1.

9 The three triangles C45, C56, C67 can next be drawn.

10 Finally, complete the development by constructing triangle CD7.

Example 2

The square is of sides 90 mm. The circle is of diameter 60 mm, the centre vertically above the mid-point of the square's base. Bottom curve of radius is 100 mm.

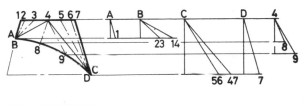

 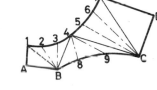

The development of the half pattern for this example follows closely the procedure as given for Example 1. Note, however, the need for six *true length diagrams* because of the need to find true lengths along the curved edges at the back and front sides of the transformer. In the three triangles required to obtain the curve in the development — B48, 489, C49 — the true lengths B8, 89 and 9C are taken directly from the front view.

Example 2

Example 3

The rectangle has sides 120 mm by 60 mm. Maximum height is 100 mm. The circle is of diameter 60 mm sloping at 30°.

In this example, again only a half pattern is needed. Each of the true lengths B1, B2, B3 and C5, C6, C7 requires its own true length construction. B4 and C4 together with the joint line true lengths A1 and D7 are taken directly from the front view.

Note: Because the circular outlet is sloping, the lengths 1–2, 3–4 and so on for the development triangles must be found on the half circle drawn with the top edge of the front view as diameter.

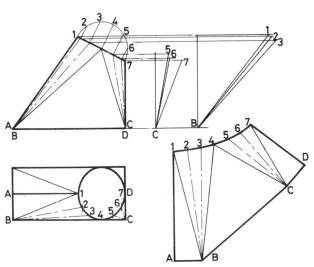

Example 3

The photographs show two further examples of sheet metal constructions involving development by triangulation.

A funnel — an example of a square to circle transformer

A fishtail nozzle

Exercises

Dimensions for the drawings shown on this page and pages 133 and 134 can be assessed by counting the sides of the 20 mm grid squares.

1   Construct a development for the oblique pyramid shown.

2   Construct a development for the frustum of the oblique pyramid.

3   Construct a development for the frustum of the oblique pyramid.

4   Develop a half pattern for the twisted square transformer.

5   Develop a half pattern for the twisted square transformer.

6   Develop a half pattern for the twisted square transformer.

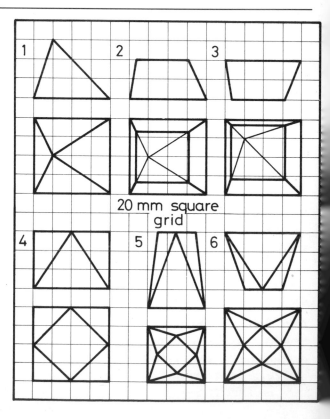

20 mm square grid

7   Develop a half pattern for the square to circle transformer.

8   Construct a half development for the square to circle transformer.

9   Construct a full development for the square to circle transformer.

10 Construct a half pattern for the rectangle to circle transformer.

11 Construct a half pattern for the rectangle to circle transformer.

12 Construct a half pattern for the rectangle to circle transformer.

13 Construct a half pattern for the circle to square transformer.

14 Construct a half development for the circle to square transformer.

15 Construct a half pattern for the circle to rectangular transformer.

16 Construct a half development for the square to circle transformer.

17 Construct a half pattern for the circle to rectangle transformer.

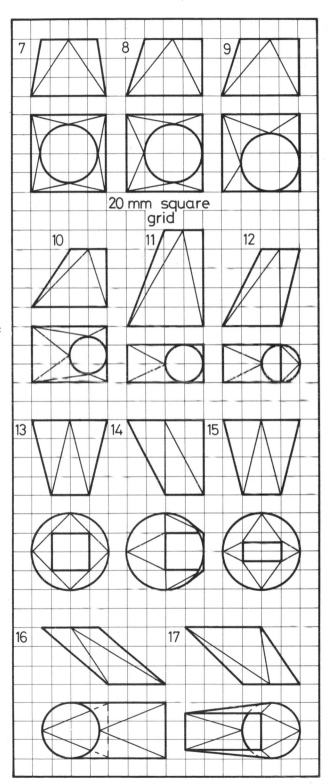

20 mm square grid

18 Develop a half pattern for the square to rectangle connector.

19 Develop a full pattern for the rectangular connector.

20 Develop a pattern for the twisted rectangular connector.

21 Develop a half pattern for the square to circle transformer.

22 Develop a half pattern for the square to circle transformer.

23 The true shape of the sloping outlet of this connector is circular. Construct a half development for the connector.

24 Develop a half pattern for the rectangle to circle connector.

25 Develop a half pattern for the rectangle to circle connector.

26 The true shape of the upper sloping face of this transformer is a circle. Develop a full pattern for the transformer.

27 A front view and plan of a rectangle to circle connector is shown. Construct a full development of its sides.

28 The true shape of the lower face of the connector shown is a circle. Develop a half pattern for the connector.

29 A front view and a plan of a rectangle to circle transformer is given. Develop a half pattern for its sides.

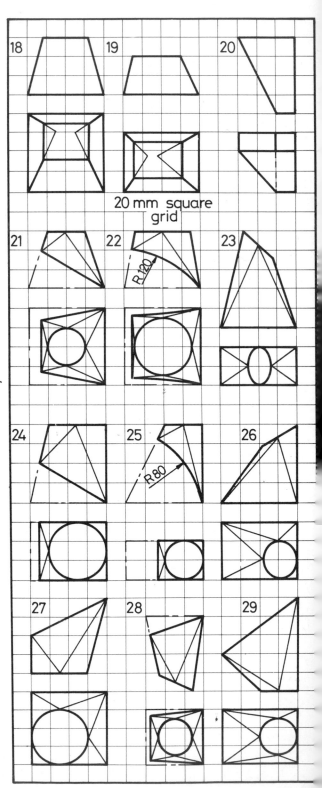

Tall cones

If the apex of a cone containing a conical part is too far from its base to allow a development to be easily constructed by radial line methods, the methods of development by triangulation can be employed.

Development of frustum of tall cone

The base diameter is 60 mm, diameter of top 36 mm, height 70 mm.

To develop a half pattern for the frustum.

1   Draw front view and plan.
2   Divide the two semicircles of the plan into six equal parts.
3   Draw on the plan the lines A1, A2, B2, B3 and so on. These lines give plans of the triangles for the development.
4   Project the lines A2, B2, B3 and so on into the front view. These lines give front views of triangles for the development.
5   Draw a true length diagram for all the lengths A2, B3, C4, D5, E6 and F7. These lines are all the same true length.
6   The true length of lines A1, B2, C3, D4, E5, F6 and G7 can be obtained from line A1 in the front view.
7   The true lengths 1–2, 3–4, 5–6 and so on, and lengths AB, BC, CD and so on, can be taken directly from the plan.
8   To construct the half pattern commence by constructing triangle A12, then AB2, followed by B23 and so on until the last triangle FG7 is constructed.
9   Now draw a fair curve through points 1 to 7 and points A to G to complete the development of the half pattern.

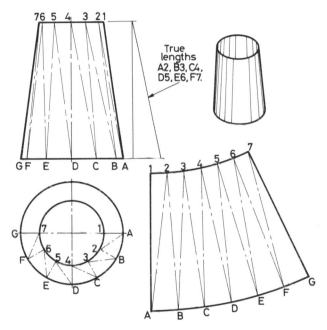

Development of frustum of tall cone

Development of truncated tall cone

The diameter of base is 60 mm, diameter of top before truncation is 28 mm, truncation at 45°.

To develop the half pattern, first construct the half pattern for the frustum before truncation. This follows the procedure explained above. True lengths of lines A1, B2, C3, D4, E5 and G6 can then be found by projecting lines from where they cross the truncation line on to line A1 on the front view. The true lengths are then taken from line A1 on the front view and transferred with a compass to the half pattern development.

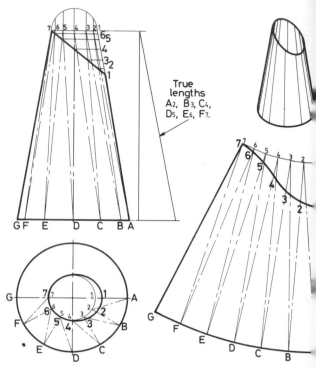

Development of truncated tall cone

Connector

Development of connector with circular outlets

Note: This is *not* part of a cone.

The diameter of the base is 60 mm, diameter of upper outlet is 56 mm, height is 90 mm.

To develop a half pattern for the connector.

1   Draw front view and plan. The circular upper opening shows as an ellipse in the plan.
2   Draw a semicircle on the upper line of the front view.
3   Divide the semicircle into six equal parts 1 to 7.
4   Project points 1 to 7 on to the upper line.
5   Project points 1 to 7 on to the ellipse in the plan.
6   Divide the semicircle of the base in the plan into six equal parts A to G.
7   Project A to G to the front view.

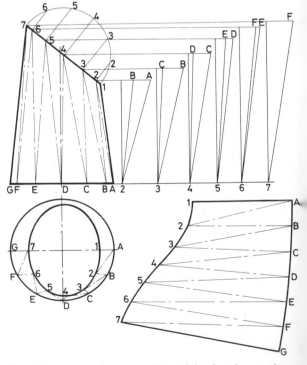

Development of connector with circular outlets

8 Now the front views and plans of all lines for the triangles required to construct the development can be drawn.

9 Draw true length diagrams for all these lines and then construct the development of the required half pattern by constructing each triangle in turn.

Tall oblique cones

Development of frustum of tall oblique cone

The base diameter is 40 mm, top diameter 32 mm, height 70 mm. Axis slopes at 75° to the base.

To develop a half pattern for the frustum:

1 Draw front view and plan.

2 Divide half the base circle and half the top circle in the plan each into six equal parts giving points A to G and 1 to 7.

3 Project the points A to G and 1 to 7 into the front view.

4 Construct the true length diagrams for all the lines A2, B2; B3, C3; C4, D4; D5, E5; E6, F6; F7. (Note that the F7 diagram is on the left of the front view because of lack of space on the right.)

5 The development for the half pattern can now be constructed from the triangles A12, AB2 and so on.

Note: Lengths AB, BC to FG and lengths 1–2, 2–3 to 6–7 on the development are taken from the divisions A to G and 1 to 7 on the plan.

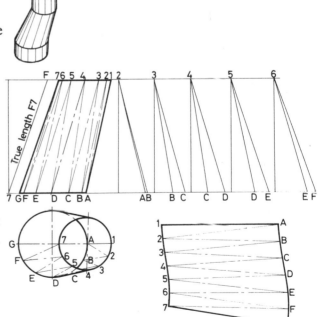

Development of frustum of tall oblique cone

Worked example

The drawings show a worked example of solutions involving all the three methods of construction for developing sheet metal parts.

A pipe A is connected by a transformer B to an outlet nozzle C. Pipe A is cylindrical. Transformer B is part of an oblique cone. Nozzle C is a truncated right cone.

PART A has been developed using *parallel line* methods.

PART B has been developed using *triangulation* methods.

PART C has been developed using *radial line* methods.

The reader is advised to study the solutions in detail.

Note: The joints between the three parts show as straight lines because they have been constructed on the principle of the common central sphere.

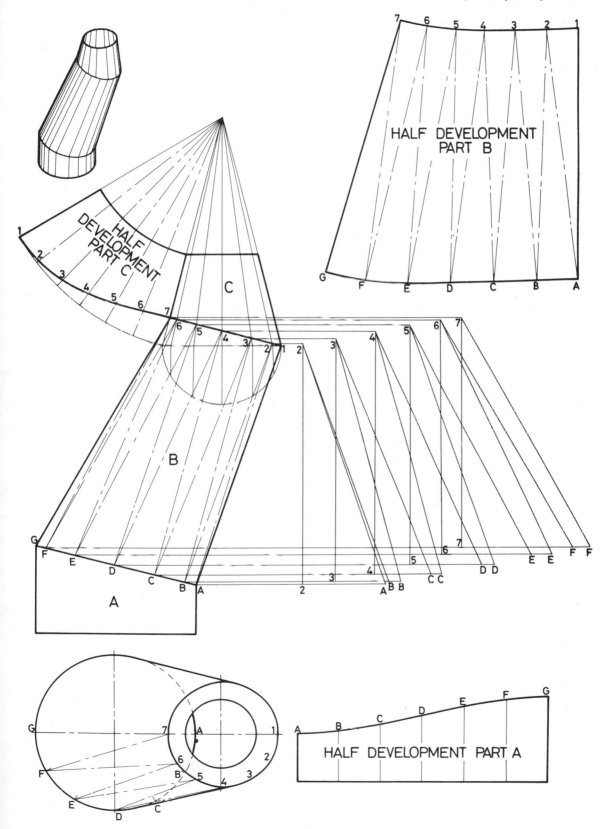

HALF DEVELOPMENT
PART B

HALF
DEVELOPMENT
PART C

C

B

A

HALF DEVELOPMENT PART A

Exercises

1 Develop, by triangulation, a half pattern for the conical connector shown. Scale 1:1.

1

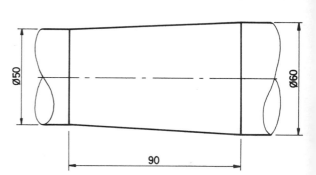

2 Develop, by triangulation, a half pattern for the conical connector working to a scale of 1:1.

2

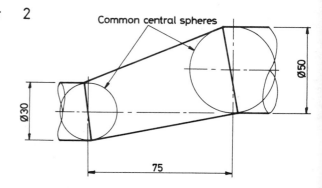

3 Develop, by triangulation methods, a half pattern for the transformer. Scale 1:1.

3

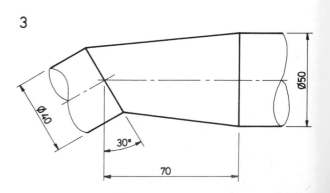

Shield and transformer

Pictorial drawings of the shield and transformer
are shown.

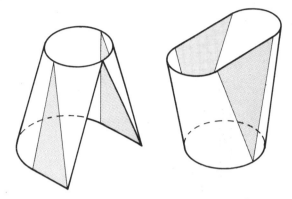

Pictorial drawings of a shield and transformer

Development of a shield
1 Divide the half circle of the top in plan into
   six equal parts to give points 1 to 7.
2 Divide the quadrant of the base into three
   equal parts giving points B, C and D.
3 In the plan join A2, A3, B5, C5, C6, D6
   and D7. Project these into the front view.
4 Construct true length diagrams as shown.
5 Commence the half development with line
   A1 — true length taken directly from the
   front view.
6 All other lengths for the triangles of the
   development are taken from the true length
   diagram or directly from the plan.

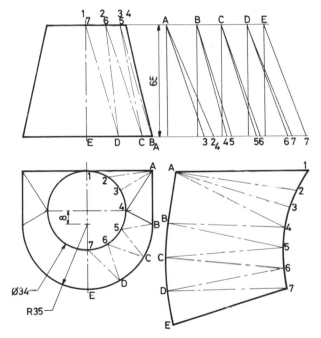

Development of a shield

Development of a transformer

1 Divide the half circle of the base in the plan into six equal parts giving points A to G.
2 Divide the half circle of the top into six equal parts giving points 1 to 7.
3 Construct true length diagrams as shown.
4 The half development can then be constructed by taking lengths for the triangle sides from either the true length diagrams or from the divisions of the half circles in the plan.

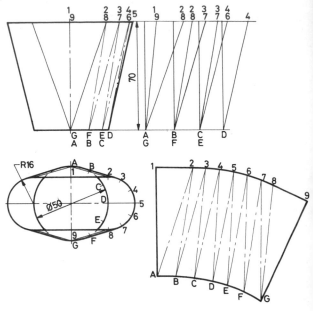

Development of a transformer

Breeches pieces

Development of breeches piece: 1
To develop a half pattern for one branch.

1 Divide half of the circle of the base in the plan into six equal parts giving A to G.
2 Divide half of the circle of one of the branches in the plan into six equal parts giving 1 to 7.
3 Project points A to G and 1 to 7 to the front view.
4 Draw lines A1, A2, to F7 and G7 on the front view.
5 Construct true length diagrams for all the true lengths as shown.
6 Construct the triangles for the half development to include points E, F and G as shown.
7 Mark off along lines E5, E6, F6, F7 and G7 the true lengths to points 5_1, 6_2, 6_1, 7_2 and 7_1 as shown.
8 Complete the half development.

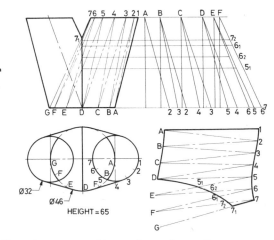

Development of breeches piece: 1

Development of breeches piece: 2

To develop a half pattern for one branch.

1 Divide half of the circle of the base in the plan into six equal parts to give A to G.
2 Draw a semicircle on the line of the upper outlet of one branch in the front view.
3 Divide this semicircle into six equal parts.
4 Project the points 2 to 6 back to the line at right angles.
5 Project the points so obtained into the ellipse of the plan giving points 1 to 7 in the plan.
6 Draw lines A2 to F7 on the front view.
7 Construct the true length diagrams as shown.
8 Construct the triangles for the half pattern to include points E, F and G.
9 Mark off along lines E5, E6, F6, F7 and G7 the true lengths to find points 5_1, 6_2, 6_1, 7_2 and 7_1 and complete the half pattern as shown.

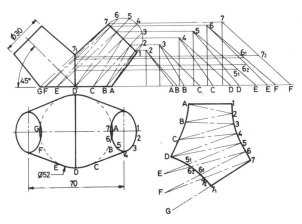

Development of breeches piece: 2

Exercises

The reader is advised to copy the given drawings to a scale of 1:1 (unless a different scale is indicated) before attempting to work the solutions.

1 The drawing shows an uptake pipe A to be connected to a horizontal pipe B by means of a tapered transformer. Develop by triangulation the pattern for the transformer to a scale of 1:5. (*City and Guilds*)

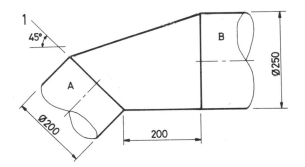

2 Develop by triangulation methods a pattern for the transformer A. Work to a scale of 1:5.

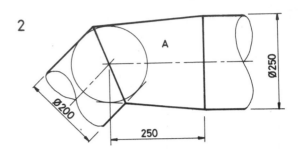

3 A front and side elevation of a gravity feed chute are shown. Develop a HALF pattern for the chute, showing clearly all construction lines. (*City and Guilds*)

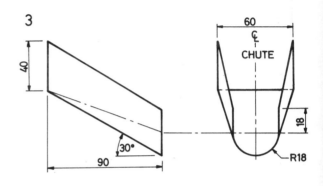

4 A connecting piece is required to join an 80 × 40 R.H.S. (Right Hollow Section) to a 50 × 30 R.H.S. twisted through 45° as shown. Develop a HALF pattern with the seams as indicated. (*City and Guilds*)

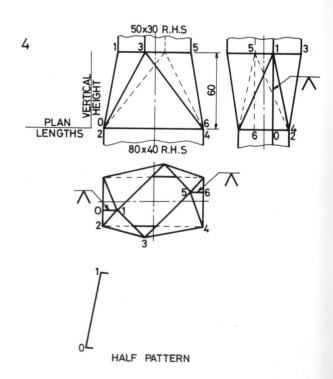

5 The drawing shows the plan and elevation of a rectangle to ellipse transformer. Triangulate a full pattern on the centre line OA, with the seam D–6 as indicated by the British Standards welding symbol. (*City and Guilds*)

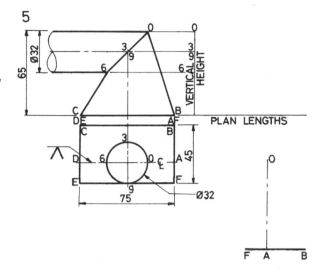

6 The drawing gives details of a two-way branch pipe. The central axes of all components are in the same plane. Using a scale of 1:5:
(a) Draw a half plan of limb A;
(b) Develop by triangulation a half pattern for this limb. (*City and Guilds*)

7 The drawing shows a delivery chute. Develop to a scale of 1:10 a pattern for the chute by triangulation using any TWO views. (*City and Guilds*)

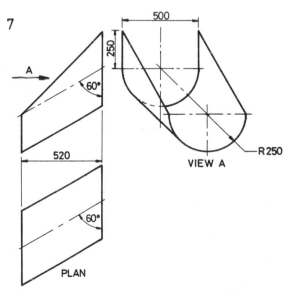

8 The drawing shows a breeches piece for a cylindrical main and equal diameter ducts. Their axes are in the same vertical plane. Draw to a scale of 1:5:

(a) A plan view of one limb of the breeches piece;

(b) Develop the pattern for this limb;

(c) Construct the true shape of the joint line XX.

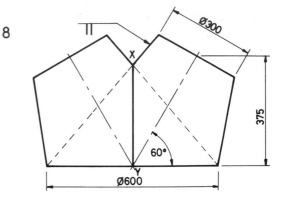

11 Scaling up development patterns to full size

When working direct from a workshop drawing the development of a pattern for a sheet metal article may have been drawn to a scale smaller than scale 1:1 (full size). It may then be necessary to scale up the pattern from the drawing to obtain the full size needed for cutting out the development on the shop floor.

Two examples of scaled up development patterns are shown.

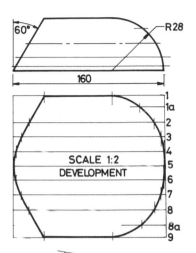

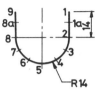

To scale up a 1:2 development to full size

This example shows a small chute, the development of which has been drawn scale 1:2. Note that this example employs the parallel line method of development.

1   Mark out a rectangle with sides of twice the length of the rectangle containing the scale 1:2 development.
2   Mark lines 1, 1a to 8a to 9 parallel with the 160 mm long sides of the scale 1:1 rectangle.

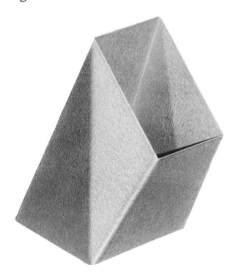

A kink-sided connector

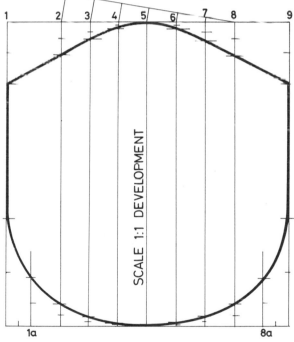

3   Measure the lengths from where the outline of the development crosses to the nearest rectangle side along lines 1 to 9.
4   Step each of these lengths *twice* along the corresponding lines 1 to 9 on the scale 1:1 drawing.
5   Join up the points so obtained to complete the development pattern.

To scale up a 1:5 development to full size

This example, on page 149, shows a square to round transformer, the pattern of which has been drawn scale 1:5. Note that this example employs triangulation methods to obtain the development pattern.

1   Mark out all the lengths required for all triangle sides, each five times as long as those on the scale 1:5 development.
2   Construct the scale 1:1 development by building up the required triangles side by side, as is usual with triangulation constructions.
3   Complete the development as shown.

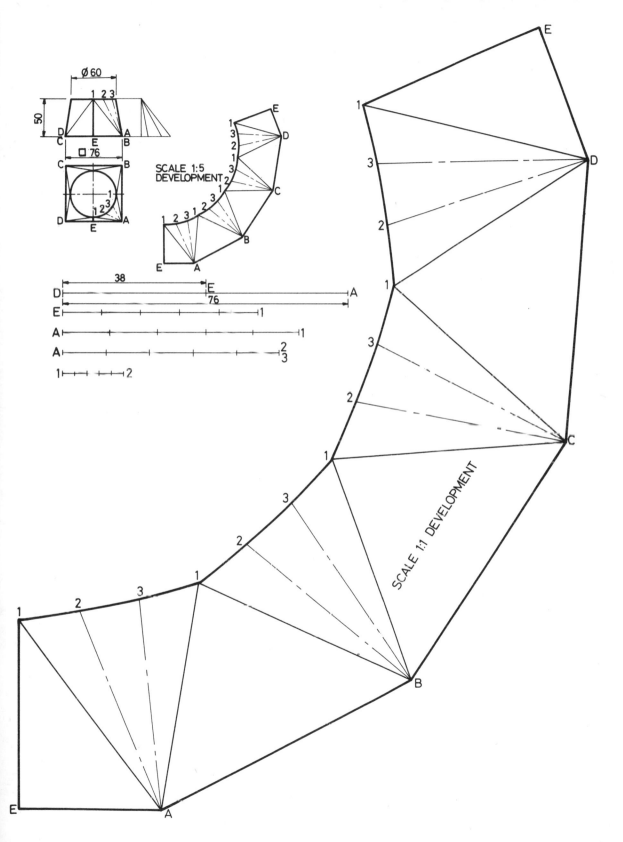

Ø 60

50

1 2 3

D
C
E
B
A

□ 76

C
B

1

1 2 3

D
E
A

SCALE 1:5
DEVELOPMENT

E
1
3
2
1
3
2
1
2 3 1 2 3
1
2 3 1
E A
D
C
B

38

D E A

76

E 1

A 1

A 2 3

1 2

SCALE 1:1 DEVELOPMENT

E
1
3
2
1
3
2
1
3
2
1
D
C
B
A
E

12 Kinked sides

Drawing 1 is a pictorial view of a hopper connected to a square duct.

Drawing 2 is a front view, end view and plan of the hopper, drawn to a larger scale.

Note that in drawing 2 the front view shows the side ABCD to be four-sided. ABCD is shown as a quadrilateral. Yet the end view of drawing 2 shows ABCD as three-sided — as a triangle.

Drawing 3 is a pictorial view of the side ABCD. Clearly something is wrong. The two sides of ABCD, AD and CD do not join up at D. In fact, the hopper could not be made as shown in drawings 1 and 2.

This is because the quadrilateral ABCD as shown in the two drawings has not been drawn so as to follow the rule:

A quadrilateral is not a plane figure unless either its sides are parallel in both planes, or unless its opposite sides will intersect if produced.

If the three drawings are now redrawn as in drawings 1A, 2A and 3A, the quadrilateral ABCD becomes two triangles and the problem of the sides meeting at D has been overcome. The quadrilateral ABCD has, in effect, been bent along diagonal AC to form two triangles ABC and ADC.

The side ABCD is said to be *kinked* along AC.

Development of parts containing sides with kinks

When developing parts containing sides with kinks the method of development by triangulation must be adopted. Examples are given on pages 151 and 152.

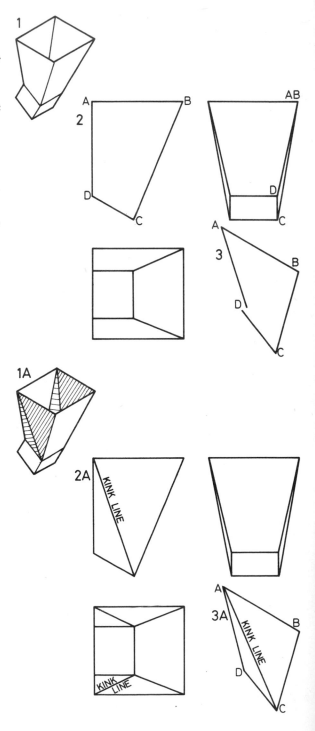

Three examples

A first example
A front view, end view and plan of a hopper
with a square top and a square outlet are
shown.

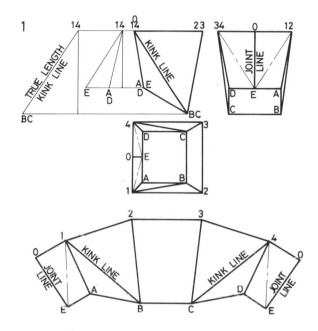

To develop a pattern for the sides of the hopper

1   Construct the true lengths of edges 1A and
    4D.
2   Construct the true length of the lines 1E
    and 4E.
3   Construct the true length of the kink lines
    1B and 4C.
4   Construct the true shape of side 23BC. Its
    vertical height is obtained from the front
    view. The lengths 23 and BC are obtained
    from the plan.
5   Construct the triangles 12B and 34C each
    side of side 23BC.
6   Then construct the triangles 1AB and 4CD.
7   Then construct the triangles 1AE and 4DE.
8   Finally, construct the triangles O1E and
    O4E to complete the pattern for the
    development.

Note: The length of the joint line OE can be
obtained from the front view.

A second example

A front view, an end view and plan of a hopper with square inlet and outlet openings are given.

To develop a pattern for its sides

1   Construct the true lengths of edges 1A and 4D.
2   Construct the true length for lines 1E and 4E.
3   Construct the true length of the kink lines 1B and 4C.
4   Construct the true shape of side 23BC. Its vertical height is taken from the front view. The lengths 23 and BC are taken from the plan.
5   Construct in turn triangles 12B and 34C; 1AB and 4CD; 1AE and 4DE; finally, O1E and O4E. The required pattern for the development is now complete.

Note: The true length of the joint line OE can be taken from the front view.

A third example

A front view and plan of a hopper with square inlet and outlet openings is given.

To develop a pattern for the sides of the hopper

1   Construct the true length of the edges 1A and 4D; the lines 1E and 4E; the kink lines 1B and 4C.
2   Construct the true shape of side 23BC as in the previous two examples.
3   Construct the triangles 12B and 34C; then 1AB and 4CD; then 1AE and 4DE; and finally O1E and O4E. This completes the development.

2

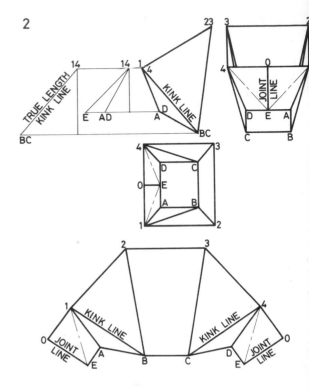

3

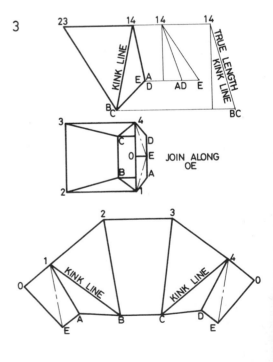

To develop a pattern for a connecting bend between two square ducts

The small-scale front view shows a bend of six segments to join a square duct of sides 100 mm long to a duct of sides 40 mm long. A half plan of segment X of the bend is also shown. The two square ducts are at right angles to each other and the radius of the centre line of the connector is 160 mm. Each segment reduces the square of the connector by 10 mm and the joins between the segments are at 15° from the centre of the arc forming the centre line.

1 Construct the true length of lines 2B, 2C and 2A.
2 Construct the true shape of the half side of the segment X. Its vertical height is taken from the given front view and the length of sides 14 and AD are taken from the half plan.
3 Construct triangles 12A, 2AB, 2BC and 23C to complete a half pattern for the development.

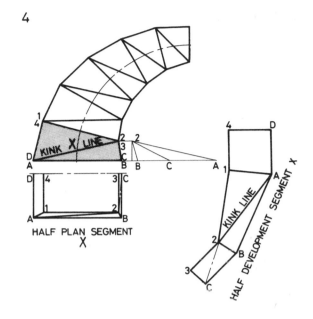

Exercises

The reader is advised to copy the given drawings to a scale of 1:1 before attempting the solutions to the exercises.

1 A kinked hopper is shown in the drawing. Develop the plate ABCD shown in the front elevation starting on the line AB. (*City and Guilds*)

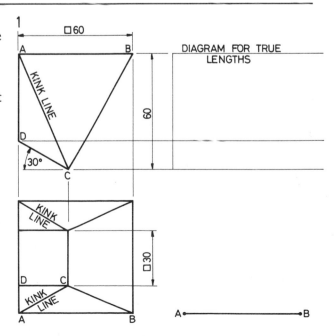

2 Develop the pattern ABCD of the hood shown using the space provided. Mark on the development the position of the kink line. (*City and Guilds*)

2

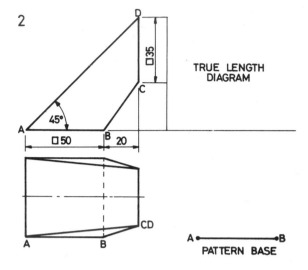

3 Determine the true shape on line X–X for the kink-sided hopper, upon the lines provided. (*City and Guilds*)

3

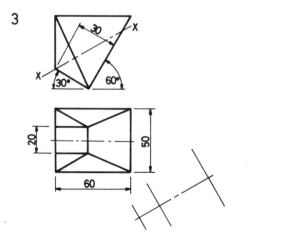

4 A front view of a connecting bend between square ducts is shown. Develop a pattern for the four sides of segment ABCD.

4

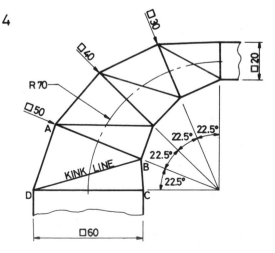

Index